Reading and Writing for Success

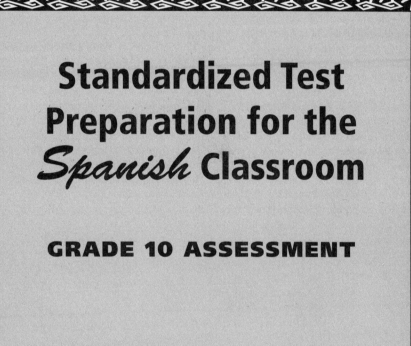

Standardized Test Preparation for the *Spanish* Classroom

GRADE 10 ASSESSMENT

Prentice Hall

Glenview, Illinois
Needham, Massachusetts
Upper Saddle River, New Jersey

ISBN 0-13-053343-2

5 6 7 8 9 10   04

Table of Contents

To the Student

Did you know that becoming a better reader in Spanish can improve your scores on standardized reading tests in English? Research has shown that the skills you develop by reading in a second language are transferred to reading in your first language. Research also shows that the more you practice for standardized tests and work on test-taking strategies, the more your scores will improve. The goal of this book is to help you improve your test-taking strategies and to provide extra practice with readings in both Spanish and English.

Getting to Know the Test

The practice tests in this book offer a variety of readings to reflect the types of passages you might expect to find on a standardized test. They also provide practice for three different types of questions you are apt to encounter on such a test: multiple choice, Short Response, and Extended Response.

Multiple Choice Multiple choice questions always have four answer choices. Pick the <u>one</u> that is the best answer. A correct answer is worth 1 point.

Short Response This symbol appears next to questions requiring short written answers:

This symbol appears next to questions requiring short written answers that are a creative extension based on the reading:

Take approximately 3 to 5 minutes to answer a Short Response question. Read all parts of the question carefully, plan your answer, then write the answer in your own words. A complete answer to a Short Response question is worth 2 points. A partial answer is worth 1 or 0 points.

NOTE: If a Short Response question is written in English, write your answer in English. If it is written in Spanish, write your answer in Spanish.

Extended Response This symbol appears next to questions requiring longer written answers based on information that can be inferred from the reading:

This symbol appears next to questions requiring longer written answers that are a creative extension based on the reading:

Take approximately 5 to 15 minutes to answer an Extended Response question. A complete answer is worth 4 points. A partial answer is worth 3, 2, 1, or 0 points.

NOTE: If an Extended Response question is written in English, write your answer in English. If it is written in Spanish, write your answer in Spanish.

Taking These Practice Tests
Your teacher will assign a test for classwork or homework. Or you might be taking these tests on your own. Each reading is followed by questions, and the Response Sheet immediately follows the questions. For multiple choice questions, you should bubble in the response. For Short and Extended Response questions, write your answers on the lines provided.

Tips for Improving Your Score

Know the Rules
Learn the rules for any test you take. For example, depending on how a test is scored, it may or may not be advisable to guess if you are not sure of the correct answer. Find that out before you begin the exam. Be sure you understand:
• how much time is allowed for the test
• the types of questions that will be asked
• how the questions should be answered
• how they will be scored

Know Yourself and Make a Plan

Ask yourself: "How will I prepare for the test?" First, ask your teacher to help you list your strengths and weaknesses on tests. Then make a detailed plan for practicing or reviewing. Give yourself plenty of time to prepare. Don't leave everything until the night before. Set aside blocks of uninterrupted time for studying, with short breaks at regular intervals.

Before the Test

Do something relaxing the night before. Then get a good night's sleep, and be sure to eat a nutritious meal before the test. Wear comfortable clothing. If possible, wear a watch or sit where you can see a clock. Make sure you have all the materials you will need. Find out in advance if you will need a certain type of pencil, for example, and bring several with you—already sharpened. Be sure you know where the test is being given and at what time. Plan to arrive early.

Know What You Are Being Asked

There are two basic types of test questions: objective, one-right-answer questions and essay questions. It is essential that you read all questions carefully. Ask yourself, "What are they asking me?" The purpose of a standardized reading test is to determine:

- how well you understand what you read
- how well you are able to use the thinking and problem-solving skills that are so critical for success in today's world

Here is a list of basic reading skills:

- Understanding major ideas, details, and organization
- Drawing conclusions
- Understanding cause and effect
- Comparing and contrasting
- Finding, interpreting, and organizing information
- Understanding author's purpose and/or viewpoint
- Understanding character and plot development

Always read the questions before you read the passage. This will help you focus on the task. If it is allowed, ask your teacher to explain any directions you do not understand.

Watch Your Time

Allot a specific amount of time per question—approximately 1 minute for multiple choice, 3 to 5 minutes for Short Response, and 5 to 15 minutes for Extended Response. Do not spend too much time on any one question, and monitor your time so that you will be able to complete the test.

Show What You Know, Relax, and Think Positively

Answer those questions that you are sure about first. If a question seems too difficult, skip it and return to it later. Remember that while some questions may seem hard, others will be easy. You may never learn to love taking tests, but you can control the situation and make sure that you reach your full potential for success.

Above all, relax. It's natural to be nervous, but think positively. Just do your best.

Multiple Choice Questions: Helpful Hints

Multiple choice questions have only one right answer. There is no "creative" response, only a correct one. This book provides extensive practice for the types of multiple choice items that you might find on a standardized reading test. There are four answer choices (A, B, C, D or F, G, H, I) per question. Allot approximately 1 minute to answer a multiple choice question. Answers are worth 1 point each.
- Read the question carefully.
- Try to identify the answer <u>before</u> you examine the choices.
- Eliminate obviously incorrect choices by lightly crossing them out.
- Try to narrow the choices down to two.
- Depending on how a test is to be scored, you may or may not want to guess (for these practice tests, check that you will **not** be penalized for guessing wrong).

Short and Extended Response: Helpful Hints

The dreaded essay question will probably not be as difficult as expected if you follow these strategies:
- Read the question <u>before</u> reading the passage.
- Re-read the question as you prepare to respond: Are you being asked to list, describe, explain, discuss, persuade, or compare and contrast? These are very different things.
- Look back at the passage as often as necessary to answer the question correctly. Underline any key sections that you think might be important to your response.
- Use the margins next to the passage to jot down thoughts and ideas and to prepare a brief outline of what you will include in your answer. Use a clear, direct introduction that answers the specific question being asked. As a start, try turning the question into a statement. Include both general ideas and specific details from the reading in your answer.

- Review your response to make sure you have expressed your thoughts well. Is your introduction clear? Have you stated the general idea(s)? Have you included supporting details?
- If your response is in Spanish, check for grammar errors (subject-verb agreement, adjective agreement, correct verb endings and tenses). In either language, proofread your answer for correct spelling.

How the Test Will Be Scored

It is important to know in advance how responses will be scored. This will lower your anxiety level and help you focus. For the purpose of these practice tests, you can assume the following:

Multiple Choice Questions

Multiple choice answers are either right or wrong. You will receive credit and 1 point if you select the correct answer.

Performance-Based Questions (Short and Extended Response)

Short and Extended Response questions are called "performance tasks." They are often scored with rubrics, which describe a range of performance. You will receive credit for how close your answers come to the desired response. The performance tasks on these practice tests will require thoughtful answers. You must:
- Read the passage
- Think about the question as it relates to the passage, and
- Explain your answer by citing general ideas and specific details from the passage

or:
- Create a written document (a letter, for example) that clearly uses or models information provided in the reading passage

Rubric for Short Response Questions

2 points   The response indicates that the student has a complete understanding of the reading concept embodied in the task. The student has provided a response that is accurate, complete, and fulfills all the requirements of the task. Necessary support and/or examples are included, and the information given is clearly text-based. Any extensions beyond the text are relevant to the task.

1 point   The response indicates that the student has a partial understanding of the reading concept embodied in the task. The student has provided a response that may include information that is essentially correct and text-based, but the information is too general or too simplistic. Some of the support and/or examples may be incomplete or omitted.

0 points   The response is inaccurate, confused, and/or irrelevant, or the student has failed to respond to the task.

Rubric for Extended Response Questions

4 points   The response indicates that the student has a thorough understanding of the reading concept embodied in the task. The student has provided a response that is accurate, complete, and fulfills all the requirements of the task. Necessary support and/or examples are included, and the information given is clearly text-based. Any extensions beyond the text are relevant to the task.

3 points   The response indicates that the student has an understanding of the reading concept embodied in the task. The student has provided a response that is accurate and fulfills all the requirements of the task, but the required support and/or details are not complete or clearly text-based.

2 points   The response indicates that the student has a partial understanding of the reading concept embodied in the task. The student has provided a response that may include information that is essentially correct and text-based, but the information is too general or too simplistic. Some of the support and/or examples and requirements of the task may be incomplete or omitted.

1 point   The response indicates that the student has very limited understanding of the reading concept embodied in the task. The response is incomplete, may exhibit many flaws, and may not address all requirements of the task.

0 points   The response is inaccurate, confused, and/or irrelevant, or the student has failed to respond to the task.

Getting Started

So let's get started. If there was anything in this Introduction that you did not understand, ask your teacher about it. Glance once again at the Helpful Hints before taking the first test. In fact, it will be helpful if you review those hints each time you take one of these tests. And remember: The more you practice, the higher your scores will be.

¡Buena suerte!

Test 1

Friendship Among Latin Americans

Adriana and Ricardo are teenagers who immigrated to Florida from the Dominican Republic and Mexico. Adriana comes from Santo Domingo, the capital of the Dominican Republic, and Ricardo from Saltillo, Mexico. They have become friends in part because they share a sense of humor and a great love of soccer, a sport they both played in their home countries.

For most young Latin Americans, two very strong influences in their lives are family and a close-knit group of friends. Adriana and Ricardo have friends from a number of Spanish-speaking countries, including Guatemala, Colombia, and El Salvador. In the group are several sets of brothers and sisters, and, as is common in Latin America, they all do things together. For example, Adriana (age 14) and her sister Elena (age 12) are very close and share their social lives as well as their family life.

Close friendships are sometimes marked by *apodos,* or nicknames, that imply a special relationship. In Mexico, for example, *primo* and *prima* ("cousin") or *hermano* and *hermana* ("brother," "sister") are commonly used. At school, Ricardo often greets Adriana in the halls with *"¡Oye, prima!"*

These friends spend free time at each other's homes and they all know each other's families. Close friends are often included in family events and celebrations. Parties that Adriana, Ricardo, and their friends attend may include several generations, from babies to grandparents.

Young people, however, must show respect to adults and are taught to treat their parents' friends courteously. They must address them with *usted.* In some countries, such as Mexico, Nicaragua, and Colombia, small children even address their parents formally. In these cases, a young child is addressed as *usted* as he or she is learning to speak. The difference between *usted* and *tú* is learned later, as they interact with playmates.

In Latin America, many children attend private schools from kindergarten through high school. Because of this, and because a family most likely will not move but will remain in the same home for many years, children who begin kindergarten together often remain classmates throughout their school career. As a result, lifelong friendships can begin at an early age.

1 Where are Adriana and Ricardo currently living?

    A.   The United States.

    B.   The Dominican Republic.

    C.   Mexico.

    D.   Adriana in Santo Domingo and Ricardo in Saltillo.

2 In the reading, which of these words do you think would be a synonym for *¡Oye!*?

    F.   *Adiós.*

    G.   *Buenas noches.*

    H.   *Hola.*

    I.   *Mucho gusto.*

3 Based on the reading, which one of the following statements is true?

    A.   When they come to the United States, Spanish speakers are friendly mostly with people who came from the same country they did.

    B.   To a Latin American, a friend is almost like a member of the family.

    C.   Latin Americans do not address each other as *tú* until they are adults.

    D.   There are no public schools in Latin America.

4 According to the reading, which of the following is a reason why lifelong friendships can be very common in Latin America?

    F.   Because most of your friends would be family members.

    G.   Because most Latin Americans have a sense of humor and share an interest in soccer.

    H.   Because you would probably go to school together from kindergarten through high school.

    I.   Because you would always treat each other courteously.

5 From an early age, Latin Americans tend to socialize with people older and younger than they are, as well as with people their own age. Describe what you think might be some advantages of this. If you think there are disadvantages, describe those as well. Use details and information from the reading to support your answer.

Nombre: _____   Fecha: _____

1 Ⓐ Ⓑ Ⓒ Ⓓ   **2** Ⓕ Ⓖ Ⓗ Ⓘ   **3** Ⓐ Ⓑ Ⓒ Ⓓ

4 Ⓕ Ⓖ Ⓗ Ⓘ

5

READ
THINK
EXPLAIN

_____

_____

_____

_____

_____

_____

_____

_____

_____

STOP

¡Hola! Me llamo Pedro

30 de septiembre

Srta. María Luisa Pardo Barros
Calle San Antonio 16
Valparaíso
Chile

Querida María Luisa:

Me llamo Peter (Pedro en español) y tengo catorce años. Soy de los Estados Unidos. Soy estudiante en Orlando, en el estado de la Florida. Hay muchas atracciones en Orlando: Por ejemplo, el famoso parque de diversiones Disney World—y Sea World también.

Soy muy deportista y me encanta nadar y patinar. Mi mamá dice que soy desordenado y que no soy nada serio. Pero sí me gusta ir a la escuela y me gusta mucho leer buenos libros. ¿Mi pasatiempo favorito? Estar con mis amigos o hablar con ellos por teléfono.

¿Cómo eres, María Luisa?

Tu amigo,

Peter (o Pedro, si el nombre español te gusta más)

1 In what city does María Luisa live?

    A. San Antonio.

    B. Valparaíso.

    C. Orlando.

    D. The reading does not say.

2 What is the English equivalent of *Querida*?

    F. Miss.

    G. Hello.

    H. Dear.

    I. It is María Luisa's first name and has no real English equivalent.

3 According to the reading, which one of the following statements might Peter make about himself?

    A. *Me gusta cocinar.*

    B. *Me gusta mucho practicar deportes.*

    C. *No me gusta nada estudiar.*

    D. *No soy ni serio ni trabajador.*

4 According to the reading, which one of the following words would Peter use to describe himself?

    F. *Gracioso.*

    G. *Perezoso.*

    H. *Sociable.*

    I. *Tacaño.*

5 Write a brief letter in Spanish to a pen pal describing yourself and what you like and don't like to do. Use the reading as a model for your letter.

Nombre: _____   Fecha: _____

1   Ⓐ   Ⓑ   Ⓒ   Ⓓ   **2**   Ⓕ   Ⓖ   Ⓗ   Ⓘ   **3**   Ⓐ   Ⓑ   Ⓒ   Ⓓ

4   Ⓕ   Ⓖ   Ⓗ   Ⓘ

5

READ
THINK
CREATE

_____

_____

_____

_____

_____

_____

_____

_____

_____

_____

STOP

Dos jóvenes
de Barcelona

En esta entrevista, nuestros amigos Ignasi Ruiz y Beatriz Segura hablan con nuestra reportera, Isabel Peña, de lo que hacen y de lo que quieren hacer en el futuro.

ISABEL: ¿Estudias o trabajas?

IGNASI: Bueno, ahora estudio inglés y también trabajo en un gimnasio, donde doy clases de ejercicio.

ISABEL: Entonces, ¿estás en muy buena forma física?

IGNASI: Sí, hago aerobic todos los días menos los domingos. También me encanta nadar. En el gimnasio tenemos una piscina muy buena. La verdad es que tenemos unas instalaciones increíbles.

ISABEL: ¿Cuáles son tus planes para el futuro?

IGNASI: Bueno, lo que más me gusta es viajar. Estudio inglés en una academia porque quiero trabajar para una línea aérea. Quiero viajar a todos los países del mundo, pero especialmente a los Estados Unidos.

ISABEL: Y en tu tiempo libre, ¿qué haces?

IGNASI: Leo mucho, especialmente novelas. También me gusta estar con mis amigos. Muchos fines de semana voy con ellos a visitar diferentes lugares de España.

ISABEL: ¿Qué estudias?

BEATRIZ: Hace tres años que estudio teatro en el Instituto de Arte Dramático de Barcelona. El año pasado actué en televisión y en algunas películas cortas. Me encanta actuar. Es lo que quiero hacer el resto de mi vida.

ISABEL: ¿Estás en forma?

BEATRIZ: Sí, claro. Para actuar es necesario estar en buena forma física. Bailo, porque también estudio danza, hago ejercicio todas las mañanas y me gustan mucho los deportes.

ISABEL: ¿Qué deportes practicas?

BEATRIZ: Estoy en un equipo de básquetbol. Practicamos los lunes y miércoles y los sábados jugamos contra otros equipos. Es muy divertido y emocionante.

ISABEL: Con todas esas actividades, ¿tienes todavía tiempo libre?

BEATRIZ: Sí, porque me organizo bien. En mi tiempo libre me gusta leer, especialmente poesía y teatro. También me gusta escuchar música clásica.

1 Why is Ignasi studying English?

    A. Because he needs it to work at the gym.

    B. Because he wants to study in the United States.

    C. Because he has a gift for learning languages.

    D. Because he wants to work for an airline.

2 Which of the following things does Beatriz <u>not</u> say about acting?

    F. She has experience acting in television and movies.

    G. She does it to stay physically fit.

    H. She loves acting and wants to do it for the rest of her life.

    I. She has been studying theater for three years.

3 What does Ignasi say about the gym where he works?

    A. That it's close to his house.

    B. That its swimming pool is not great.

    C. That it's not open on Sundays.

    D. That it has incredible facilities.

4 Why does Beatriz say she has free time in spite of all her activities?

    F. Because she has a lot of energy and gets things done quickly.

    G. Because she is well organized.

    H. Because she knows her limits and when to drop an activity that's taking too much of her time.

    I. Because she makes free time a priority.

5 READ THINK EXPLAIN Based on the article, how are Ignasi and Beatriz each preparing for their goal in life?

6 READ THINK EXPLAIN Describe a Ignasi y Beatriz. Usa detalles e información del artículo.

Nombre: _____ Fecha: _____

1 Ⓐ Ⓑ Ⓒ Ⓓ   **2** Ⓕ Ⓖ Ⓗ Ⓘ   **3** Ⓐ Ⓑ Ⓒ Ⓓ

4 Ⓕ Ⓖ Ⓗ Ⓘ

5

READ
THINK
EXPLAIN

_____
_____
_____
_____
_____

6

READ
THINK
EXPLAIN

_____
_____
_____
_____
_____
_____
_____
_____

STOP

The High-School Experience in Latin America

How does the high-school experience in Latin America compare with that in the U.S.? There are many similarities, but there are also some noticeable differences.

A normal course load for a high-school student in the U.S. is usually between five and eight subjects a year, but in Latin America students are more likely to take between ten and twelve. These classes do not, however, meet every day. A class might meet only two or three times a week, which is more similar to schedules in U.S. colleges and universities. As a result, there is more variation in students' day-to-day schedules. In addition, although physical education is taught, team sports are not part of the curriculum. On the other hand, English is mandatory in many schools. Because foreign language study is much more common in Latin American schools, the average student is fluent in Spanish and at least one or two other languages by the time he or she graduates from high school.

Classes in Latin American schools are also structured very differently than those in the U.S. Lecturing is the preferred format and there tends to be less student participation. Although extracurricular activities are offered, they are far less common than they are in schools in the U.S.

It is unusual for Latin American schools to have the amenities, such as lockers, that students in the U.S. take for granted. As a result, students must carry their

> **Classes in Latin American schools are also structured very differently than those in the U.S. Lecturing is the preferred format and there tends to be less student participation.**

backpacks and book bags with them throughout the school day. Since Latin American students tend to have much more homework than American students, these accessories come in handy.

While letter grades are routinely used in the U.S., they are rarely used in Latin America. Although the grading scale varies from country to country, numerical grades, such as 1–10 or 1–20, are the norm.

Private schools are common in Latin America and a large number of these are operated by the Roman Catholic Church. Although parochial schools are not usually coeducational, there are many coed private schools that are not affiliated with any church. Because many of these schools are associated with certain ethnic or cultural traditions, students must study the appropriate foreign language, usually American English, German, British English, Italian, or French.

One of the most noticeable differences between the U.S. school system and that in Latin America is that students in Latin America are frequently required to wear uniforms. While the uniform is sometimes the same throughout the country, it is more likely identified with a certain school. The girls' uniform is usually a jumper, a blouse, and a tie, or a pleated skirt, a blouse, and a vest or blazer. Boys wear slacks, a shirt and tie, and sometimes a sweater or blazer as well.

1 How does the average number of classes per year compare for U.S. and Latin American students?

    A. Latin American students take more classes than U.S. students.

    B. Latin American students take fewer classes than U.S. students.

    C. Latin American and U.S. students take the same number of classes.

    D. Latin American and U.S. students take the same number of classes, but in Latin America classes only meet three days a week.

2 Based on the reading, why are backpacks and book bags so important for Latin American students?

    F. Because they are expensive and would cost a lot to replace.

    G. Because they are a status symbol.

    H. Because they don't have lockers for their books.

    I. Because they don't have shelves for their books.

3 How do church-affiliated schools in Latin America differ from private schools?

    A. They are usually coeducational.

    B. They are <u>not</u> usually coeducational.

    C. They require that students study another language.

    D. They are not common in Latin America.

4 How does the grading system in Latin America differ from that used in the U.S.?

    F. Numerical grades are rarely used.

    G. Numerical grades are regularly used.

    H. Letter grades are usually used.

    I. Letter grades are never used.

5 **READ THINK EXPLAIN** Why do you think English is mandatory in Latin American schools? Use details and information from the reading to support your answer.

Nombre: _____   Fecha: _____

1 Ⓐ Ⓑ Ⓒ Ⓓ   **2** Ⓕ Ⓖ Ⓗ Ⓘ   **3** Ⓐ Ⓑ Ⓒ Ⓓ

4 Ⓕ Ⓖ Ⓗ Ⓘ

5

READ
THINK
EXPLAIN

_____

_____

_____

_____

_____

_____

STOP

A popular bilingual teen magazine is including a feature in the next issue on what the school day is like for high-school students throughout the U.S. Read what this student has to say about a typical day at her school.

Mi día escolar

Me llamo Carmen y soy estudiante en la escuela secundaria El Toro en El Toro, California. Mi día escolar empieza a las siete y cincuenta y termina a las dos y media.

En la primera hora tengo español, mi clase favorita. Me gusta hablar español.

En la segunda hora tengo matemáticas. Mi profesora de matemáticas enseña muy bien y me gusta mucho la clase.

Mi clase de ciencias es a las nueve y veinte. No tengo mucha tarea en mi clase de ciencias y mi profesor es muy gracioso.

En la cuarta hora tengo inglés. Me gusta la clase y mi profesora de inglés es mi profesora favorita.

Tengo almuerzo a las diez y cincuenta.

En la sexta hora tengo mi clase de literatura. Me gusta mucho leer.

Mi clase de educación física es a las doce y veinte. No es mi clase favorita, pero soy deportista y me gusta practicar deportes.

En la octava hora tengo historia. A mi profesora de historia le gusta mucho enseñar y es una clase muy interesante.

Tengo mi clase de computadoras a la una y cincuenta. No es muy interesante y no me gusta nada.

1 What time does Carmen's first class begin?

    A. 7:50 A.M.

    B. 9:20 A.M.

    C. 10:20 A.M.

    D. 2:30 P.M.

2 According to the reading, why does Carmen like her math class so much?

    F. Because her teacher doesn't give much homework.

    G. Because it's right before lunch.

    H. Because she has a very good teacher.

    I. Because it isn't difficult for her.

3 Who is Carmen's favorite teacher?

    A. Her Spanish teacher.

    B. Her science teacher.

    C. Her math teacher.

    D. Her English teacher.

4 Which class is Carmen's least favorite?

    F. Her computer class.

    G. Her science class.

    H. Her physical education class.

    I. Her history class.

5 **READ THINK EXPLAIN** Based on what you know about Carmen, what kinds of factors influence whether she likes a class or not?

Nombre: _____   Fecha: _____

1 Ⓐ   Ⓑ   Ⓒ   Ⓓ   **2** Ⓕ   Ⓖ   Ⓗ   Ⓘ   **3** Ⓐ   Ⓑ   Ⓒ   Ⓓ

4 Ⓕ   Ⓖ   Ⓗ   Ⓘ

5

READ
THINK
EXPLAIN

_____

_____

_____

_____

_____

_____

STOP

¿POR QUÉ *está tan* **nervioso?**

Son las seis y media de la mañana y Marcos está preparándose para el primer día de clases en su nueva escuela. Decide llevar sus tenis nuevos, jeans y una camiseta negra.

—Buenos días, Marcos.

—Buenos días, mamá.

—¿Cómo estás?

—Estoy un poco nervioso, mamá.

—No te preocupes. Todo va a estar bien. ¿Tienes todo lo que necesitas en tu mochila?

—Sí, tengo dos bolígrafos, cuatro lápices, un cuaderno, una carpeta de argollas, una calculadora y una regla.

—Eres muy ordenado, hijo. Pues, es la hora de salir para la escuela.

Cuando Marcos entra en la sala de clases para su clase de primera hora, una estudiante le dice:

—Hola. Me llamo Carolina. ¿Y tú?

—Me llamo Marcos.

—Mucho gusto, Marcos.

—Igualmente, Carolina. ¿De dónde eres?

—Soy de Panamá. ¿Y tú?

—Soy de Perú.

—¿Qué clases tienes?

—Tengo álgebra, historia, español, inglés, biología, literatura, educación física y arte.

—¿A qué hora tienes almuerzo, Marcos?

—En la cuarta hora.

—Yo también. Pues, ¿te gustaría comer el almuerzo conmigo y con algunos de mis amigos? La cafetería tiene un buen bufet de ensaladas y toda clase de sandwiches.

—Sí, me gustaría mucho.

Después de su clase de tercera hora, Marcos entra en la cafetería donde están Carolina y sus amigos, Ramón, Javier, María, David y Linda.

Todos hablan sobre sus clases y sus actividades extracurriculares. Ramón es miembro de la banda y toca el saxofón. También juega béisbol. Javier juega fútbol americano y practica artes marciales. María hace gimnasia y también es bailarina. David juega básquetbol y trabaja en un supermercado. Linda juega fútbol y es presidenta del consejo estudiantil. Y Carolina escribe para la revista literaria, canta en el coro y juega vóleibol.

—Marcos, ¿qué actividades te interesan más?—le dice Ramón.

—Pues, toco la trompeta y me gustaría ser miembro de la banda. También me encanta jugar tenis. ¿Tienen un equipo de tenis en esta escuela?

—¡Claro que sí! Y es uno de los mejores equipos de tenis de nuestra división—le responde Linda.

—Mañana a las tres de la tarde, hay una reunión en el auditorio donde se puede aprender más sobre todas las actividades extracurriculares de la escuela. ¿Por qué no vienes con nosotros?—le dice Javier.

—Bueno. Voy a estar allí.

—Entonces mañana todos nosotros vamos a comer el almuerzo y después de las clases vamos a la reunión—les dice David.

Cuando terminan de comer el almuerzo, todos dicen "adiós" y salen para llegar a tiempo a su próxima clase.

Cuando Marcos regresa a casa, está cansado pero muy contento porque a él le gusta mucho su nueva escuela. También le gustan sus nuevos compañeros de clase. Quiere participar en unas de las actividades extracurriculares de su escuela y también se interesa en trabajar de tutor en álgebra.

1 Why is Marcos so nervous?

   A. He has lost his class schedule.

   B. It's his first day at a new school.

   C. He can't find his backpack.

   D. He doesn't have all of his school supplies.

2 According to the story, what happens when Marcos arrives at school?

   F. He has breakfast in the cafeteria.

   G. He realizes that he's forgotten his backpack.

   H. A classmate introduces herself to him.

   I. He realizes that he's late for class.

3 What was discussed during Marcos's lunch with Carolina and her friends?

   A. Their classes and extracurricular activities.

   B. Their favorite musical instruments.

   C. Their favorite foods.

   D. The meeting that was held to discuss school activities.

4 How does Marcos feel at the end of the day?

   F. He's tired from playing tennis.

   G. He's happy because the students are friendly and the school has a lot to offer.

   H. He's happy because he has a student to tutor in algebra.

   I. He's happy because he has signed up for band and the tennis team.

5 | READ THINK EXPLAIN | ¿Cómo son los nuevos amigos de Marcos?

6 | READ THINK EXPLAIN | Imagina que eres un(a) nuevo(a) estudiante en una de las escuelas en tu ciudad o pueblo. Haz una lista de todo lo que debes hacer para que tu primer día vaya bien.

Test 6

1 Ⓐ Ⓑ Ⓒ Ⓓ **2** Ⓕ Ⓖ Ⓗ Ⓘ **3** Ⓐ Ⓑ Ⓒ Ⓓ

4 Ⓕ Ⓖ Ⓗ Ⓘ

5

READ
THINK
EXPLAIN

_____
_____
_____
_____
_____
_____

6

READ
THINK
EXPLAIN

_____
_____
_____
_____
_____
_____
_____
_____
_____

STOP

Leisure Activities

PASO A PASO 1	PASO A PASO 2	PASO A PASO 3
Chapter 3	Chapter 4	

Test **7**

Aztec Games and Rituals

A god of games?! The ancient Aztecs of Mexico had just such a god: Macuilxóchitl (ma-quill-SO-chi-tul), which tells us something about the importance of games in the Aztec culture. And their games were not simply pastimes; they had religious significance as well.

Pelota was the forerunner of all present-day games that are played with a rubber ball. It was played on a large, H-shaped court. The ball was extremely hard, so hard that the players had to wear padded clothing for protection. They were allowed to hit the ball only with their elbows, hips, and knees. The object of the game was to knock the ball through a stone ring at either end of the court. The team of the first person to succeed in doing this won the game. And it was very important to win, for the team that lost was sacrificed!

Patolli was a very different type of game, much more enjoyable for all concerned and very popular. It was a board game similar to parcheesi played on a cross-shaped board. Specially marked beans were used as dice. Twelve differently colored counters were divided among the players, who moved them around the board depending upon the throw of the dice.

One of the most dramatic of the Aztec rituals was also a ritual for many other indigenous groups. It is still performed by the Totonac Indians of Papantla, a village near Veracruz, Mexico. It is the ancient ritual of the *voladores,* or fliers. It survives to this day because the Spanish missionaries did not forbid it. They did not realize that it was a religious ritual and not just a dangerous sport.

Picture a pole a hundred feet high. At its top is a platform on which five men stand in costumes decorated with brightly colored feathers. One man is playing a flute. The other four suddenly leap into the air. You gasp, then realize that each of them is attached to the top of the pole by a rope tied around the ankles. As they fall, the ropes unravel, causing them to

circle the pole. The length of the ropes is such that each *volador* flies around the pole thirteen times before landing on the ground.

The calendar was at the center of Aztec life. Perhaps the four *voladores* originally represented the four seasons, each with thirteen weeks (the thirteen circuits of the pole). Or the total number of circuits (13) that the *voladores* (4) make may have represented the 52 years that made up a cycle in the ancient sacred calendar. Today, however, it is not the religious aspect of the event, but its spectacular grace and daring that excite us.

1 The Aztec game of *pelota* has elements of two modern games in it. Which ones?

    A.   Soccer and baseball.

    B.   Basketball and baseball.

    C.   Volleyball and soccer.

    D.   Soccer and basketball.

2 The Aztec game of *pelota* could still be played today exactly as it was originally, but one element of the game would have to be changed. What is that element?

    F.   The players would have to wear unpadded clothing.

    G.   Both men and women would have to be allowed to play.

    H.   The losing team would have to be allowed to go home after the game.

    I.   The court would have to be shaped like the letter E.

3 What present-day sport is most comparable to the ritual of the *voladores*?

    A.   High diving.

    B.   Bungee jumping.

    C.   Skateboarding.

    D.   Rappeling.

4 Why is it that we can still see the *voladores* perform today?

    F.   Because it was not just an Aztec ritual.

    G.   Because the Spanish missionaries enjoyed the grace and daring of the dangerous sport.

    H.   Because the missionaries didn't understand what was happening.

    I.   Because the missionaries encouraged religious rituals.

5 Imagine that an image of Macuilxóchitl is going to be used as an icon for all sports and games in the United States today. They have announced a contest to design the icon. Describe Macuilxóchitl as you would design him and explain how you made your design decisions. Use details and information from the article in your answer.

Nombre: _____   Fecha: _____

1 Ⓐ Ⓑ Ⓒ Ⓓ   **2** Ⓕ Ⓖ Ⓗ Ⓘ   **3** Ⓐ Ⓑ Ⓒ Ⓓ

4 Ⓕ Ⓖ Ⓗ Ⓘ

5

READ
THINK
EXPLAIN

_____

_____

_____

_____

_____

_____

_____

_____

_____

_____

STOP

Una conversación difícil

Es viernes por la noche. Generalmente me gusta estar con mis amigos los fines de semana. ¿Adónde vamos mis amigos y yo? Al centro comercial. Al cine. Al parque, donde jugamos fútbol americano o, en el invierno, al gimnasio, donde jugamos básquetbol o vóleibol.

Pero mañana, no. Mañana me gustaría ir de pesca con papá. Es su cumpleaños.

—¿Papá?

—¿Sí, Roberto?

—Papá, me gustaría . . .

—Sí, Roberto. Te gustaría ir al parque de diversiones. Lo siento, pero estoy cansado.

—No, papá. Quiero ir al campo con . . .

—A ver . . . Quieres ir al campo con Ramón y su familia mañana. Estoy ocupado, Roberto. Puedes hablar con tu mamá . . .

—¡No, no, papá! Quiero ir de pesca . . .

—¿De pesca? ¿Cómo vas a ir de pesca? No puedes ir solo. ¿Con quién vas a ir de pesca?

—Contigo, papá. Quiero celebrar tu cumpleaños contigo.

—¿Conmigo? ¿Mi cumpleaños? ¡No me digas!

—¿No vas a estar ni cansado ni ocupado, papá?

—No, no, Roberto. ¿Quién puede estar cansado en su cumpleaños? Pero sí voy a estar ocupado. Voy a ir de pesca contigo.

1 What is different about this weekend?

    A. Roberto is going to the mall with his friends.

    B. Roberto is going either to the park or to the gym with his friends.

    C. It is his birthday.

    D. It is his father's birthday.

2 Why doesn't Roberto's father want to go to the amusement park?

    F. Because he's tired.

    G. Because he's sick.

    H. Because he's busy.

    I. Because it's Friday evening.

3 Why does Roberto want to go to the country?

    A. To be with Ramón and his family.

    B. To go fishing with his father.

    C. So he can talk to his mother.

    D. Because it's his birthday.

4 Which of the following would you say is the best reason why Roberto's father is so happy at the end of the story?

    F. Because he loves to go fishing.

    G. Because he isn't tired or busy anymore.

    H. Because Roberto wants to spend the day with him.

    I. Because tomorrow is his birthday.

5 This year Roberto probably has not bought his father a birthday present. As far as his father is concerned, however, Roberto is giving him the best gift possible. There is a common English expression that says "it's the thought that counts." Briefly explain the expression and give an example.

Test 8

1 Ⓐ Ⓑ Ⓒ Ⓓ   **2** Ⓕ Ⓖ Ⓗ Ⓘ   **3** Ⓐ Ⓑ Ⓒ Ⓓ

4 Ⓕ Ⓖ Ⓗ Ⓘ

5

READ
THINK
EXPLAIN

_____

_____

_____

_____

_____

_____

STOP

Campeón de ajedrez

Joan* Santana es un joven dominicano que vive en Teaneck, New Jersey. Es estudiante de secundaria y quiere estudiar medicina para ser pediatra. Le gustan el béisbol, básquetbol y fútbol, y también las computadoras.

Pero Joan tiene otro pasatiempo muy especial que, para algunas personas, lo hace un *whiz kid*. Es todo un campeón de ajedrez, y su biografía y recomendaciones sobre el juego están en el libro, *Whiz Kids Teach Chess*, por Eric Schiller.

Joan tiene una carrera bastante larga como campeón de ajedrez. En 1995, como representante de los Estados Unidos, triunfó sobre sus rivales en el Torneo Internacional por Equipos que tuvo lugar en Islandia. En 1999, fue uno de treinta y ocho jóvenes jugadores escogidos para el Pressman All-America Chess Team. La United States Chess Federation estableció este equipo en 1987 para los mejores jóvenes jugadores de ajedrez en los Estados Unidos.

¿Cuál es el secreto de Joan para ser campeón de ajedrez? ¿Es realmente un genio? ¿Tiene padres que se dedican sólo a él y sus campeonatos? Joan se describe simplemente como una persona tranquila que practica unas cuatro horas al día. "Para llegar a aprender todo lo que sé," dice, "tuve que estudiar y trabajar mucho." Sus héroes y modelos son dos grandes del ajedrez: el cubano José Raúl Casablanca y el ruso Anatoli Karpov.

Según Joan, ser campeón de ajedrez también lo ayuda a triunfar en otras situaciones. Por ejemplo, Joan saca muy buenas notas en la escuela. Dice que esto es resultado de jugar ajedrez, porque sabe concentrarse y pensar con disciplina. Y también gracias al ajedrez, Joan sabe que siempre tiene que trabajar mucho. Para Joan, éste es el ingrediente secreto para triunfar, y con este ingrediente todo el mundo puede ser un gran maestro. ◆

* "Joan" es la forma de "Juan" en catalán, un idioma parecido al francés y al español que se habla en Cataluña, una región en el noreste de España.

1 According to the article, what does Joan want to do for a career?

    A. He wants to be a pediatrician.

    B. He wants to be a grand master at chess.

    C. He wants to be an author of books on chess.

    D. He wants to be a computer programmer.

2 How does Joan say he learned everything he knows about chess?

    F. From the author Eric Schiller.

    G. From his heroes, José Raúl Casablanca and Anatoli Karpov.

    H. From his parents, who devoted themselves to him and his championships.

    I. From practicing several hours a day, studying, and working hard.

3 What kind of person does Joan say he is?

    A. Peaceful.

    B. A "whiz kid."

    C. Competitive.

    D. A grand master at chess.

4 According to Joan, in what other ways has being a chess champion been helpful to him?

    F. He's made a lot of friends.

    G. It's taught him concentration and discipline, so that he gets good grades.

    H. He's won a lot of championships.

    I. He's been included in *Whiz Kids Teach Chess*.

5 **READ THINK EXPLAIN** ¿Qué pregunta te gustaría hacerle a Joan? Usa detalles e información del artículo para formular tu pregunta.

6 **READ THINK EXPLAIN** ¿Crees que todo el mundo puede ser un gran maestro si trabaja mucho? ¿Por que sí o no?

Nombre: _____   Fecha: _____

1 Ⓐ Ⓑ Ⓒ Ⓓ   **2** Ⓕ Ⓖ Ⓗ Ⓘ   **3** Ⓐ Ⓑ Ⓒ Ⓓ

4 Ⓕ Ⓖ Ⓗ Ⓘ

5

READ
THINK
EXPLAIN

_____
_____
_____
_____
_____
_____

6

READ
THINK
EXPLAIN

_____
_____
_____
_____
_____
_____
_____
_____
_____

STOP

The Hidden Corn: A Mayan Legend

Long ago, corn was hidden inside a large rock and no one knew that it was there. One day, a group of black ants saw a tiny crack in the rock and crawled inside, where they found the corn and tasted it. It was so good that they carried out some kernels to eat later. However, a few of the kernels were too heavy to carry far, so the ants left them behind.

Fox came by and found the kernels. He quickly ate them and exclaimed, "How delicious! Now if I could only find some more!" All day long, Fox stayed near the place where he'd found the kernels, looking for more. Finally, when the sun was almost gone and there was just a thin glow of gold left on the horizon, Fox saw the ants making their way to the rock. They entered the tiny crack and later came out loaded down with kernels of corn. After they had left, Fox pried at the crack, but he couldn't get inside the rock. Again he had to be content with eating the kernels the ants could not carry away.

When Fox returned home, all the other animals saw how happy and well fed he was. They asked him why, but Fox would not say. So the animals made a plan to find out. That night, they followed Fox to the rock. They saw him eating the corn and they tried it too. "How delicious!" they exclaimed. When they found out that the black ants were bringing the corn out from the rock, they asked them if they would

bring out more. The ants agreed but found that they could not bring out nearly enough for all the animals.

So the animals asked the red ants and the rat to help, but neither could fit through the crack. Finally, they went to Man and said, "If you will help us, we will give you the secret of this delicious food." Man asked the thunder gods for help, and they sent for Yaluk, the most powerful.

Yaluk asked the woodpecker to tap on the thinnest part of the rock and then hide his head. In an instant, Yaluk tossed down

a great lightning bolt at the spot where the woodpecker had tapped. The rock burst open, and thousands of golden ears of corn poured out.

And so it was that Man and all the animals received the gift of corn. The only unfortunate thing was that when Yaluk threw down his lightning bolt, the woodpecker forgot to hide his head. A piece of rock hit him and his head began to bleed. That is why to this day the woodpecker has a red head.

1 How did Fox first find the corn?

    A. He saw the black ants carrying the kernels.

    B. He found some kernels lying on the ground.

    C. He saw it through a tiny crack in the rock where it was hidden.

    D. He stepped on the rock where it was hidden.

2 At the beginning of the story, Fox and the black ants are the only ones enjoying the gift of corn. Who is enjoying it at the end?

    F. The red ants and the rat.

    G. Yaluk and the other thunder gods.

    H. Man and all the animals.

    I. Woodpecker.

3 In a "just so" story, such as "How the Leopard Got His Spots," a fact of nature is explained through the events in the story. Look at the following lines from this legend and pick the one that sounds like part of a "just so" story.

    A. "Fox pried at the crack, but he couldn't get inside the rock."

    B. "Man asked the thunder gods for help."

    C. "Yaluk tossed down a great lightning bolt."

    D. "The woodpecker has a red head."

4 Why do you think this legend calls corn a "gift"?

    F. Because corn was a very important food for the Mayas.

    G. Because corn is the color of gold.

    H. Because corn is so rare and needs special conditions to grow.

    I. Because gift-giving is very important in the Mayan culture.

5 Choose a passage in this story in which the visual imagery is especially vivid. Explain why you chose this passage.

Nombre: _____   Fecha: _____

1 Ⓐ Ⓑ Ⓒ Ⓓ   **2** Ⓕ Ⓖ Ⓗ Ⓘ   **3** Ⓐ Ⓑ Ⓒ Ⓓ

4 Ⓕ Ⓖ Ⓗ Ⓘ

5

READ
THINK
EXPLAIN

_____
_____
_____
_____
_____
_____
_____
_____
_____
_____

STOP

Frutas y verduras
de América

Hay muchas frutas y verduras de América que hoy se comen en todos los países del mundo. Las más importantes son el tomate, la papa, el maíz, los frijoles, muchas variedades de chiles y el cacao. Estas frutas y verduras son muy nutritivas, se pueden preparar fácilmente y son muy sabrosas.

En el pasado, sólo era posible comer muchas frutas de América en las regiones tropicales. Pero gracias a las técnicas modernas de refrigeración, ahora es posible comprar muchas de estas frutas— papayas, piñas, guayabas, mangos y otras—en los Estados Unidos y Canadá.

Test 11

1 According to the reading, why are so many foods from America eaten throughout the world today?

    A.   Because they are very inexpensive.

    B.   Because they are nutritious, easy to prepare, and delicious.

    C.   Because they are low in calories.

    D.   Because they are high in carbohydrates.

2 Why is it possible to buy many of the fruits mentioned in the reading in the U.S. and Canada now?

    F.   Because refrigeration has made it possible to keep them fresh.

    G.   Because other countries are now allowed to export them.

    H.   Because they are so much in demand.

    I.   Because they are cheaper than fruits grown in this country.

3 What kind of climate is necessary to grow fruits such as papayas, pineapples, guayabas, and mangoes?

    A.   Temperate.

    B.   Tropical.

    C.   Polar.

    D.   Desert.

4 **READ THINK EXPLAIN** Name some countries where you think papayas, pineapples, guayabas, and mangoes might be grown. Why did you choose these?

Nombre: _____   Fecha: _____

1 Ⓐ Ⓑ Ⓒ Ⓓ   **2** Ⓕ Ⓖ Ⓗ Ⓘ   **3** Ⓐ Ⓑ Ⓒ Ⓓ

4

READ
THINK
EXPLAIN

_____

_____

_____

_____

_____

_____

STOP

La comida argentina

A los argentinos les encanta la carne. Este gran gusto por la carne es resultado directo de la historia y geografía de Argentina. Cuando los españoles llegaron al país, trajeron caballos y ganado (vacas y toros). Transformaron las pampas—las grandes tierras fértiles en el centro de Argentina—en enormes ranchos de ganado. Allí trabajan los gauchos, la versión argentina de los *cowboys* en los Estados Unidos, y de allí viene la carne que los argentinos preparan de muchas maneras sabrosas.

Para los argentinos, "carne" quiere decir sólo carne de res, no de pollo, cordero o puerco. El plato más típico de Argentina es el asado. Este plato, que se come en todas las celebraciones, se prepara en un fuego de carbón o leña. Se sirve con una salsa picante que se llama chimichurri (una mezcla de ajo, aceite de olivo, vinagre y cilantro) y una ensalada.

Por supuesto, los argentinos también comen pollo, cordero y puerco. Pero, igual que los americanos, llaman estos tipos de carne por su nombre. La cocina argentina también tiene una gran variedad regional y étnica que refleja la diversidad de su población. La comida italiana es la influencia más importante, pero también es fácil encontrar restaurantes que sirven comida típica de otras partes del mundo (norte y este de Europa, Oriente Medio y Asia).

Si todavía tienes hambre después de comer estas comidas, no te olvides de probar algunos de los dulces argentinos. El dulce más típico se llama dulce de leche. Se hace con leche y azúcar y es similar a la mantequilla de cacahuate. Se pone encima de pan tostado, en pasteles, o se come simplemente con una cuchara. Si no te gusta el dulce de leche, puedes probar el flan o los helados. En Argentina los helados son muy buenos, por la influencia italiana.

¡Es evidente que vas a comer bien si vas a Argentina!

1 How did the Spaniards most influence Argentine cuisine?

    A. They brought crops that were not native to the area.

    B. They turned the pampas into vast cattle ranches.

    C. They were very open to teaching and learning from the native people.

    D. They encouraged immigrant farmers to settle in frontier areas.

2 When Argentines use the word *carne*, what kind of meat are they talking about?

    F. Beef.

    G. Beef, lamb, pork, and chicken.

    H. Beef and pork.

    I. Beef and lamb.

3 Which country has had the greatest influence on Argentine cuisine?

    A. France.

    B. Germany.

    C. Italy.

    D. The United States.

4 According to the reading, what food does the *dulce de leche* resemble?

    F. Ice cream.

    G. *Flan.*

    H. Peanut butter.

    I. Marmalade.

5 **READ THINK EXPLAIN** ¿Cómo son similares la cocina argentina y la cocina americana? ¿Cómo son diferentes? Usa detalles e información de la lectura en tu respuesta.

Nombre: _____ Fecha: _____

1 Ⓐ Ⓑ Ⓒ Ⓓ   **2** Ⓕ Ⓖ Ⓗ Ⓘ   **3** Ⓐ Ⓑ Ⓒ Ⓓ

4 Ⓕ Ⓖ Ⓗ Ⓘ

5

READ
THINK
EXPLAIN

_____

_____

_____

_____

_____

_____

STOP

Families and Celebrations

PASO A PASO 1	PASO A PASO 2	PASO A PASO 3
Chapter 5	Chapter 6	

Test 13

Holidays
IN THE Hispanic World

Some holidays are celebrated differently in Latin America and Spain than in the United States. *La Nochebuena,* or Christmas Eve, for example, is when most of the Spanish-speaking world celebrates Christmas. A nativity scene *(un nacimiento* or *un pesebre)* is a common decoration in homes. It may be small—the Dominican Republic is famous for its truly miniature figures—or large enough to fill an entire room or patio. But large or small, it is often very elaborate, with hills, trees, roads, little houses, and small mirrors to represent ponds. *El nacimiento* is usually the focal point of the festivities, with family gathered around to sing carols to the accompaniment of a guitar or a bamboo pipe or maracas. Colored paper lanterns, balloons, piñatas, and dancing are often part of the evening celebration.

Epiphany *(el Día de los Reyes),* on January 6, marks the formal end of the Christmas holidays. Traditionally, it was the day on which children in Spanish-speaking countries received their gifts, because it commemorates the arrival of the Three Kings into Bethlehem with their gifts of frankincense, gold, and myrrh. Today, however, in more and more homes, gifts are opened on Christmas itself or on Christmas Eve.

In much of Latin America, the weather is warm during the end-of-year holidays (below the equator it is the beginning of summer) and *el Año Nuevo* may be celebrated with fireworks and even barbecues. In Spain, it is the custom to eat twelve grapes at the stroke of midnight, one grape each time the clock chimes.

El Día de la Raza, October 12, celebrates the blending of the Spanish and indigenous cultures that resulted from Columbus's landing in the Americas. It is sometimes called *el Día de la Hispanidad.* In recent years, however, it has become of less importance than specific national holidays. *El Día de la Independencia* is, of course, celebrated on different days in different countries. For example, September 15 is the national holiday of four Central American nations: Guatemala, Honduras, El Salvador, and Nicaragua. Paraguay celebrates its independence from Spain on May 14; Argentina, May 25; Venezuela, July 5; Colombia, July 20; Peru, July 28; Bolivia, August 6; Ecuador, August 10; Mexico, September 16; and Chile and Costa Rica, September 18. The Dominican Republic celebrates its independence from Haiti on February 27; Uruguay, its independence from Brazil on August 25; Panama, its independence from Colombia on November 3. And Spain's national holiday? *El Día de la Hispanidad*—October 12.

Another major fall holiday is *el Día de los Muertos* on November 2. This holiday—known as All Souls' Day in English—is a day of remembrance for all those who have died. It is celebrated especially vividly in Mexico. There are, of course, prayers, religious services, and visits to the cemetery, and families build special altars, called *ofrendas,* in their homes. These *ofrendas* are decorated with flowers and candles, but they are not at all solemn. Photographs of loved ones who have died are displayed among objects that they cherished or used most—a rocking chair, for example, or reading glasses, gardening tools, or cooking utensils. *El Día de los Muertos* is also celebrated by eating a sweet

bread—*el pan de muerto*—which is either shaped like skulls and crosses or decorated with them, and white sugar candies in the shape of skulls, crosses, coffins, and tombs. For children there are white masks, tin or wire skeletons attached to strings, and even toy coffins that contain a skeleton that jumps out when a string is pulled.

In the calendar of the Catholic Church, almost every day is dedicated to one or more saints. A person's "saint's day," or *santo,* is the day dedicated to the saint who has that person's name (or one derived from it). For example, *el santo* for every José, Josefina, or Josefa is St. Joseph's Day (March 19), and *el santo* for every Pablo, Paulo, Paulina, and Paula is St. Paul's Day (June 29). Traditionally, part of a person's name was determined by the saint's day on which he or she was born. For example, if a girl whose family planned to name her María Luisa happened to be born on May 30—St. Ferdinand's Day—she would likely be named María Luisa Fernanda to honor that saint. In fact, the traditional Mexican "Happy Birthday" song, *Las Mañanitas,* is actually a song for a saint's day.

This custom is disappearing, however, and a person's birthday and saint's day are often not the same. In many countries, a person's saint's day is considered more important than a birthday. Even non-Catholics may celebrate their *santo,* for no one wants to miss out on his or her special day for a party and a few gifts. So truly every day is *un día de fiesta en el mundo hispano.*

1 In a traditional Latin American home, which of the following most closely compares with the Christmas tree in a traditional U.S. home?

  A.   *La Nochebuena.*
  B.   *El nacimiento.*
  C.   *La piñata.*
  D.   *El Día de los Reyes.*

2 Which one of the following statements is true?

  F.   All of the nations of Central America have the same Independence Day.
  G.   In the U.S., the best-known national holiday among the Latin American nations is *el cinco de mayo.*
  H.   Of the nations of Latin America, all but two celebrate their national holiday within the five-month period from May to September.
  I.   All of the Spanish-speaking countries of Latin America got their independence from Spain.

3 Though we celebrate it quite differently, what holiday in the U.S. has the same underlying purpose as *el Día de los Muertos?*

  A.   The Fourth of July.
  B.   Memorial Day.
  C.   Labor Day.
  D.   Veterans' Day.

4 Complete this statement: Today a person's *santo* is most often. . .

  F.   That saint's birthday.
  G.   His or her own birthday.
  H.   The day dedicated to the saint who has the same or a similar name.
  I.   Either March 19, May 30, or June 29.

5 READ THINK EXPLAIN — October 12 was once a fairly major holiday throughout the Americas. Why do you suppose that in most countries the national holiday has become of greater importance than Columbus Day? Do you think this is a good thing or a bad thing? Why?

6 READ THINK EXPLAIN — If you live far to the north or to the south of the equator, there are considerable differences in the way in which you might celebrate the end-of-year holidays. Explain why and describe at least three of those differences.

Nombre: _____   Fecha: _____

1 Ⓐ Ⓑ Ⓒ Ⓓ   **2** Ⓕ Ⓖ Ⓗ Ⓘ   **3** Ⓐ Ⓑ Ⓒ Ⓓ

4 Ⓕ Ⓖ Ⓗ Ⓘ

5

READ
THINK
EXPLAIN

_____
_____
_____
_____
_____
_____
_____

6

READ
THINK
EXPLAIN

_____
_____
_____
_____
_____
_____
_____
_____
_____
_____

STOP

EL SOL, viernes 18 de julio

NOTICIAS DE CELEBRACIONES

Esta semana en San Antonio muchas familias celebran ocasiones muy especiales.

Quinceañera

Mirella Lugo Armas, hija de Humberto Lugo Díaz y Carmen Armas Garza de Lugo, celebra sus quince años el domingo 20 de julio a las 6:00 P.M. en el restaurante Casa Estrella. Hay una gran fiesta con una banda de música tejana.

Boda

Dolores Lara Villarreal y Roberto Pastor Peña celebran su boda en la iglesia de San Antonio, el sábado 19 de julio a las 8:00 P.M. Después de la ceremonia hay una fiesta con música y una cena en casa de la familia Lara.

Día del santo

Jaime José Paredes Sánchez celebra el día de su santo el viernes 25 de julio. Hay una comida en su honor en casa de sus padrinos a las 2:00 P.M.

Graduación

Ana Luisa Martínez Puente celebra su graduación de la Memorial High School el día 22 de julio. Después de la graduación hay una barbacoa para la familia y los amigos en el parque Fiesta Texas a las 4:00 P.M.

Cincuenta años

Roberto González Juárez y María Luisa Gallardo Correa de González celebran su aniversario de bodas el 25 de julio en el salón de fiestas La Suerte. Van a celebrar la ocasión con una comida deliciosa para la familia y los amigos.

1 Which of the celebrations has a party outside?

    A. Cincuenta años.

    B. Graduación.

    C. Día del santo.

    D. Quinceañera.

2 What do all of the notices of celebrations have in common?

    F. They all mention food.

    G. They all mention music.

    H. They all take place in the evening.

    I. They all mention a ceremony.

3 Which of these occasions is celebrated only in the Hispanic culture?

    A. Boda.

    B. Cincuenta años.

    C. Quinceañera.

    D. Graduación.

4 Which of the celebrations mentions the names of the parents of the honored person or people?

    F. Graduación.

    G. Quinceañera.

    H. Día del santo.

    I. Boda.

5 READ THINK EXPLAIN Which of these celebrations do you think might have more guests that are family members than friends? Why do you think these celebrations might be more for family members?

6 READ THINK EXPLAIN Clasifica las fiestas en una escala de 5 a 1, con 5 para la fiesta más formal, y 1 para la fiesta menos formal. Explica tus clasificaciones "5" y "1."

Nombre: _____ Fecha: _____

1 Ⓐ Ⓑ Ⓒ Ⓓ   **2** Ⓕ Ⓖ Ⓗ Ⓘ   **3** Ⓐ Ⓑ Ⓒ Ⓓ

4 Ⓕ Ⓖ Ⓗ Ⓘ

5

READ
THINK
EXPLAIN

_____
_____
_____
_____
_____
_____

6

READ
THINK
EXPLAIN

_____
_____
_____
_____
_____
_____
_____
_____
_____
_____

STOP

Cambios en la familia española tradicional

A principios del siglo XX, había en la familia típica española: Un papá que salía a trabajar; una mamá que se dedicaba sólo a los hijos y a los quehaceres; y siete u ocho hijos (de quienes tres o cuatro morirían muy joven). En su casa también vivían parientes de varias generaciones. Los bisabuelos, abuelos y algunas tías solteras eran algunos de los parientes que vivían en la casa con la familia típica española. Y en el verano, tíos, tías y primos llegaban para pasar parte de sus vacaciones con la familia.

La esperanza de vida para los españoles en 1900 era muy baja: Un hombre podía esperar vivir hasta los 34 años, y una mujer hasta los 36. Según la cultura hispana, la familia tenía un valor enorme. Los españoles, como los hispanos en todo el mundo, consideraban que la familia era lo más importante en la vida, y guardaban para ella sus sentimientos más fuertes de amor, respeto, fidelidad y responsabilidad.

En el siglo XX mucho cambió, pero no todo. Los papás todavía salen a trabajar y la familia todavía tiene muchísima importancia. Pero dos cosas tuvieron un impacto enorme en la familia española: La esperanza de vida subió dramáticamente, y muchas mujeres empezaron a trabajar fuera de casa.

Hoy día los españoles tienen una esperanza de vida más del doble de lo que era a principios del siglo XX. La esperanza de vida para los hombres es 73 años, y 81 para las mujeres. Los abuelos no viven en la casa de los hijos para ayudar a cuidar a los nietos y hacer otros quehaceres. Al contrario, viven en sus propias casas y tienen sus propios trabajos.

En muchos casos, los hijos adultos se quedan en la casa de sus padres. Según la revista española *Muy interesante,* un fenómeno "típicamente español" es la familia con hijos de 28 o 30 años que todavía viven con sus padres. Una causa de este fenómeno es que no hay suficientes empleos para los jóvenes, y por eso no tienen dinero para conseguir sus propias casas. Pero otra causa es que es difícil independizarse, y los hijos quieren seguir disfrutando del estatus económico y del cariño que reciben en la casa de sus padres.

Muchos cambios profundos resultaron de la entrada de las mujeres a los trabajos fuera de casa. Por ejemplo, el número de hijos en la familia típica española bajó dramáticamente. Hasta los últimos 25 años del siglo, la familia típica todavía tenía siete u ocho hijos. En 1974, nacieron 682.010 niños en España, más que en ningún otro año del siglo. Pero en 1975 comenzó a bajar el número de nacimientos. A fines del siglo, España era el país con menos nacimientos por año en todo el mundo, con 1.18 hijos por pareja.

En España, como en muchos países, el papel de la mujer cambió muchísimo en el siglo XX. Pero muchos aspectos del papel tradicional de la mujer española no cambiaron. Los hijos y la casa todavía se consideran principalmente responsabilidades de la mujer. Sí, las mujeres pueden trabajar fuera de casa. Pero según un estudio del Instituto de la Mujer, en el 85 por ciento de las familias españolas las mujeres son las que aseguran que todo en casa funcione bien—cuidado de los niños, comidas y limpieza.

1 According to the article, which traditional value in the Spanish culture has <u>not</u> changed?

    A. Having many children.

    B. The importance of family.

    C. Women being occupied only with their families.

    D. Grandparents acting as caretakers for their children's family.

2 According to the article, why are young people in Spain waiting so long before they move out of their parents' homes?

    F. Jobs are scarce, so they can't afford their own homes.

    G. There aren't enough houses.

    H. They need to help support their parents.

    I. It's against tradition for young people to move out until they are married.

3 When was the Spanish birth rate at its lowest point?

    A. At the beginning of the twentieth century.

    B. In the 1950s.

    C. In the 1970s.

    D. At the end of the twentieth century.

4 What was the finding of the study conducted by Spain's Instituto de la Mujer?

    F. That women are experiencing tremendous stress running their households and working outside the home.

    G. That the great majority of women are still responsible for running the household.

    H. That women are having fewer babies.

    I. That women are happiest working outside the home.

5 ¿Por qué crees que la esperanza de vida cambió tan dramáticamente en el siglo XX?

6 Name some of the advantages and disadvantages of typical family life in Spain at the beginning of the twentieth century. Use details and information from the article to support your answer.

Nombre: _____ Fecha: _____

1 Ⓐ Ⓑ Ⓒ Ⓓ   **2** Ⓕ Ⓖ Ⓗ Ⓘ   **3** Ⓐ Ⓑ Ⓒ Ⓓ

4 Ⓕ Ⓖ Ⓗ Ⓘ

5

| READ |
| THINK |
| EXPLAIN |

_____
_____
_____
_____
_____
_____

6

| READ |
| THINK |
| EXPLAIN |

_____
_____
_____
_____
_____
_____
_____
_____
_____

STOP

A CULTURE *as Seen Through Its* Textiles

On July 26, 1925, archaeologists made a dramatic discovery in the desert of the Paracas peninsula, approximately 150 miles south of the Peruvian capital of Lima. In the desert off the Pacific coast they found an underground network of tombs from the Paracas and Nazca cultures that dated back to the fourth century B.C. Such a group of elaborately interconnected tombs is sometimes called a necropolis, a Greek word meaning "city of the dead." The Paracas necropolis contained beautiful, richly decorated gold objects, along with hundreds of perfectly preserved human bodies carefully wrapped in intricately woven, embroidered cloth that was as well preserved as the bodies it contained.

Woven cloth, or textiles, has of course played both a practical and a ceremonial role in world cultures for thousands of years. The textiles found at Paracas were probably specially made for use in burials and almost surely revealed the social status of the people buried there.

Images woven into garments or added to them were a form of communication in ancient cultures. Whether painted, embroidered, or decorated with metal or brightly colored feathers, many textiles contained important symbolic information. The most common images found on the Paracas textiles were those of birds, cats, snakes, rodents, llamas, and fish. By showing the animals that were native to the region, these pictures represented in one way or another the three basic realms of nature that daily affected the people who made them: the sky, the earth, and the sea. Human forms were also shown. Altogether, the pictures no doubt reflected concepts important to the people's culture, such as nature gods, who the individual's ancestors were, or his or her own social status.

Today, people in Peru and neighboring Bolivia continue to weave ponchos, tunics, and hats that use some of the same designs found in their people's textiles over two thousand years ago.

1 What is Paracas?

    A. Another name for Peru.

    B. A Peruvian peninsula and the name of a people that once lived there.

    C. The capital of Peru.

    D. A type of Peruvian textile.

2 What is a necropolis?

    F. A desert in Peru.

    G. A place for storing ancient gold objects.

    H. A vast underground burial site.

    I. A type of Greek city.

3 Which one of the following statements is <u>not</u> true?

    A. The modern textiles of Peru are totally different from those found in ancient tombs.

    B. The people of Peru still use many of the same design elements that their ancestors did.

    C. Weaving is a very ancient art.

    D. The tombs in Paracas were discovered in the twentieth century.

4 Why were images included in the textiles of ancient peoples?

    F. For purely religious reasons.

    G. To communicate information of some sort.

    H. To preserve the body of the person around whom it was wrapped.

    I. To impress visitors to the tombs.

5 **READ THINK EXPLAIN** "Woven cloth, or textiles, has . . . played both a practical and a ceremonial role in world cultures for thousands of years." Make a list of three "Practical" and three "Ceremonial" uses of textiles today.

6 **READ THINK EXPLAIN** Choose any well-known person and describe the textile that you would design for his or her burial cloth. Describe the symbols (colors, objects, figures) that you would use and explain why you chose them.

Nombre: _____   Fecha: _____

1 Ⓐ Ⓑ Ⓒ Ⓓ   **2** Ⓕ Ⓖ Ⓗ Ⓘ   **3** Ⓐ Ⓑ Ⓒ Ⓓ

4 Ⓕ Ⓖ Ⓗ Ⓘ

5
READ
THINK
EXPLAIN

_____
_____
_____
_____
_____
_____

6
READ
THINK
EXPLAIN

_____
_____
_____
_____
_____
_____
_____
_____

STOP

Necesito comprar ropa

¿Te gusta ir de compras, pero no te gusta estar con muchas personas? Lee esta historia de la solución de Margarita para este problema.

Margarita, una joven argentina de dieciséis años, tiene un problema. Necesita comprar ropa para sus vacaciones en Chile, pero está muy ocupada. También no le gusta nada ir al centro comercial porque siempre hay muchas personas por allí. Decide visitar uno de los sitios en la Internet para buscar la ropa que necesita.

Primero, Margarita busca un sitio donde se especializan en ropa para jóvenes. El sitio que más le gusta tiene un catálogo con toda clase de ropa moderna. En la página principal, hay información sobre cómo seleccionar el departamento de donde quiere comprar unos artículos. Esa página indica cómo pagar por lo que compra y cómo comunicarse con la compañía. También incluye información sobre garantías, liquidaciones, y qué opciones tiene si no le gusta lo que compra.

Margarita selecciona dos pares de jeans, tres camisetas de diferentes colores, dos pares de pantalones cortos, un suéter negro, una sudadera morada, una chaqueta y unos tenis. También compra el especial de la semana, una minifalda azul que cuesta sólo veinte pesos. ¡Qué ganga!

Luego, Margarita tiene una pregunta: "¿Cómo puedo determinar si esta ropa y estos zapatos me van a quedar bien?" Decide consultar la página donde incluyen información para ayudar a los clientes a determinar esto.

Después, Margarita decide pagar por toda la ropa con su tarjeta de crédito, pero tiene otra pregunta: "¿Garantiza este sitio la protección de mi información personal?" Consulta otra página donde informan a los clientes que sí hay protección.

Cuando el paquete llega a su casa, Margarita está muy contenta con la ropa que compró. Toda le queda bien y los colores son brillantes.

© Prentice-Hall, Inc.

1 What is Margarita's problem?

    A. She needs clothes for her vacation but doesn't have enough money to buy them.

    B. She needs clothes for her vacation but doesn't like to shop in crowded malls.

    C. She needs to replace the clothes that she lost during her vacation.

    D. She needs to buy vacation clothes before the stores close.

2 What type of information is <u>not</u> mentioned on the main page of the Web site that Margarita consults?

    F. How to pay for your purchases.

    G. How to choose the department you're interested in.

    H. Which items are on sale.

    I. Which items are no longer available.

3 According to the story, why is Margarita concerned about ordering from an online catalog?

    A. She's worried that she won't receive the items on time.

    B. She's worried that her personal information might not be protected.

    C. She's worried that she can't return the items if she's unhappy with them.

    D. She's worried that the items might look different from the way they look in the catalog.

4 How does Margarita feel after the package arrives?

    F. Unhappy because it didn't arrive on time.

    G. Unhappy because the clothes did not fit well.

    H. Happy because the clothes fit well and the colors were bright.

    I. Happy because the company included a special gift in the package.

5 [READ THINK EXPLAIN] ¿Prefieres ir de compras en el centro comercial o en la Internet? ¿Por qué?

6 [READ THINK CREATE] Imagina que vas a crear un sitio en la Internet para ropa deportiva para jóvenes. Inventa un nombre para el sitio, decide qué tipo de información vas a incluir en la página principal, qué tipos de fotos o dibujos vas a incluir y cuánto cuesta cada artículo de ropa. En tu hoja de papel, dibuja la página principal de tu sitio. Debes dibujar una página atractiva que a los estudiantes de tu escuela les gustaría visitar.

© Prentice-Hall, Inc.

Nombre: _____ Fecha: _____

1 Ⓐ Ⓑ Ⓒ Ⓓ   **2** Ⓕ Ⓖ Ⓗ Ⓘ   **3** Ⓐ Ⓑ Ⓒ Ⓓ

4 Ⓕ Ⓖ Ⓗ Ⓘ

5

READ
THINK
EXPLAIN

_____
_____
_____
_____
_____
_____

6

READ
THINK
CREATE

_____
_____
_____
_____
_____
_____
_____
_____
_____

STOP

La moda lo permite todo

A veces, cuando miramos fotos y revistas viejas, nos parece extraña la ropa que la gente llevaba. ¿Realmente pensaban que esos diseños, colores o telas eran atractivos? ¿Cómo podían llevar los hombres corbatas con esas rayas tan feas? Y las mujeres con sus vestidos largos con ese diseño de flores—¡qué horror! ¿No tenía espejos esa gente?

La respuesta en realidad es muy sencilla: claro que tenían espejos, y se miraban en ellos, y les gustaba mucho lo que veían, porque ésa era la moda.

Y la moda, como ya debemos saber, lo permite todo. Cada año hay nuevos estilos de ropa. Pero curiosamente, algunos de los estilos de hace varias décadas están de moda hoy día. ¿Ves algunos de los estilos siguientes en tu escuela . . . o los llevas tú?

La ropa negra de los beatniks

En los años cincuenta, algunos jóvenes son *beatniks,* y llevan sólo ropa negra. Los muchachos y las muchachas se visten igual, con pantalones, suéteres de cuello alto, botas y chaquetas de cuero. Mucha gente asocia esta ropa con delincuentes juveniles. En realidad, los *beatniks* son artísticos e intelectuales, con inclinación por la poesía, música y política.

Las minifaldas y las botas go-go

A mediados de los años sesenta, las minifaldas están de moda. Son un cambio muy dramático en la moda, porque antes las muchachas sólo llevaban vestidos y faldas a la rodilla o más largos. Para completar su *look,* las muchachas llevan las botas *go-go,* que generalmente son blancas. Los colores más populares para la ropa son tonos fuertes y "psicodélicos" de rosa, verde, anaranjado y morado.

Los vestidos granny y las camisetas tie-dye

A fines de los años sesenta y a principios de los setenta, muchos jóvenes son *hippies.* Las muchachas llevan vestidos largos con diseños exóticos de la India, o los vestidos *granny,* que imitan el estilo de la ropa de las pioneras americanas. Las camisetas *tie-dye* también son muy populares para las muchachas y los muchachos.

Los zapatos con plataforma

En los años setenta, los zapatos con plataforma están de moda. Estos zapatos son magníficos para las personas que quieren ser más altas. ¡Y son ideales para caminar cuando llueve!

Los jeans

Antes de los años sesenta, los jeans no se ven mucho en las ciudades. Pero en esa década, los estudiantes de universidad empiezan a llevarlos más y más. Los *hippies* llevan los jeans acampanados y—por tanto uso— con agujeros. En los años ochenta y noventa, muchos jóvenes compran jeans nuevos bastante caros y, cuando llegan a su casa, los cortan y les hacen agujeros. Esto es un escándalo para sus padres, que no comprenden por qué sus hijos arruinan su ropa nueva de esta manera.

1 After reading this article, what do you think is meant by the title, *"La moda lo permite todo"*?

    A. Some things never go out of fashion.

    B. People will wear whatever is in fashion.

    C. Fashion always breaks new ground.

    D. Fashions come and go.

2 Why does the author ask if the people in earlier decades had mirrors?

    F. Because in photos from those periods the men's ties always looked badly frayed.

    G. Because the women's skirts used to be so long.

    H. Because it's hard to believe people used to dress that way if they knew how they looked.

    I. Because strange designs always look even more peculiar in a mirror than in reality.

3 According to the article, why were miniskirts such a dramatic change in women's fashion?

    A. Because previously skirt lengths had been to the knee or below.

    B. Because they came in psychedelic colors.

    C. Because the general public did not approve of them.

    D. Because they gave women more freedom of movement.

4 In the eighties and nineties, why would parents get upset when their children made holes in their jeans?

    F. Because the jeans looked ugly with holes in them.

    G. Because the jeans weren't good for cold weather.

    H. Because the holes made their children look poor and neglected.

    I. Because the jeans were brand new.

5 **READ THINK EXPLAIN** ¿Qué moda de antes no quieres ver nunca más? ¿Por qué no te gusta esa moda?

6 **READ THINK EXPLAIN** Which of the fashions described do you think also made a political or philosophical statement? Explain your answer.

Nombre: _____   Fecha: _____

1 Ⓐ Ⓑ Ⓒ Ⓓ   **2** Ⓕ Ⓖ Ⓗ Ⓘ   **3** Ⓐ Ⓑ Ⓒ Ⓓ

4 Ⓕ Ⓖ Ⓗ Ⓘ

5

READ
THINK
EXPLAIN

_____

_____

_____

_____

_____

_____

6

READ
THINK
EXPLAIN

_____

_____

_____

_____

_____

_____

_____

_____

_____

STOP

FATHER Junípero Serra *and the* *First* California Missions

Between 1769 and 1782, Junípero Serra, a Franciscan missionary, founded the first nine missions in what is today the state of California: San Diego de Alcalá (1769), San Carlos Borromeo de Carmelo (1770), San Antonio de Padua (1771), San Gabriel Arcángel (1771), San Luis Obispo (1772), San Francisco de Asís (1776), San Juan Capistrano (1776), Santa Clara de Asís (1777), and San Buenaventura (1782). These missions were the beginnings of what are today several important cities and tourist attractions: San Diego, Carmel, San Gabriel, San Luis Obispo, San Francisco, San Juan Capistrano, Santa Clara, and Ventura.

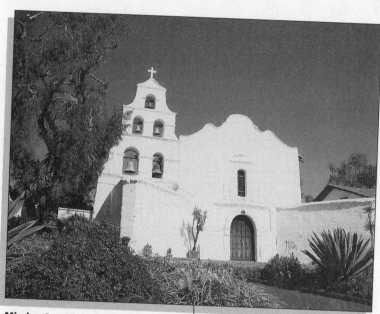

Mission San Diego de Alcalá

Father Serra was following the highly successful mission system that had been in place since the earliest days of Spanish exploration in the Americas. In the southeastern United States it extended from Florida up to North Carolina and in the southwest, from Texas to California. Through this system, Catholic priests received financial and military support from the Spanish Crown to build missions where the priests could convert the indigenous people not only to the Catholic faith but also to the Spanish way of life. The priests were protected by Spanish soldiers as new lands were claimed, although very often these two groups disagreed about the best way to treat the new converts. Father Serra, for example, was known for his efforts to protect his converts from the soldiers' violence and corruption.

Father Serra was born Miguel José de Serra in 1713 to a poor farming family on Spain's Mediterranean island of Mallorca. At the age of sixteen, he entered a Franciscan monastery to study for the priesthood. After a year, he entered the order of Franciscan Friars and changed his name to "Junípero," one of St. Francis of Assisi's most compassionate and faithful followers. He was a professor of theology at Lullian University in the island's capital city of Palma de Mallorca until 1749, when he volunteered for a missionary post in Mexico. For eighteen years, Father Serra served as a missionary in outposts, villages, and mining camps throughout central

© Prentice-Hall, Inc.

Mexico. Some of these years included prolonged stays in Mexico City, where he trained other priests for missionary work.

In 1767, King Carlos III expelled Jesuit missionaries from their missions in Baja California. Father Serra was chosen to replace them. He was there only a year when he received orders to travel with a military expedition to what was then called "Alta California." Carlos III was eager to have this Spanish territory settled because explorers from Russia, England, and Holland were becoming interested in it. In late June 1769, after a treacherous three-month trip through a thousand miles of mountains, jungles, and deserts, Father Serra reached

the place that would become his first mission in this territory. Today, this mission still stands in the city that grew around it and took its name: San Diego.

The missions that Father Serra founded are about thirty miles apart from each other along the southern California coast. This was a distance that could be covered in a day's journey on foot. The dirt road that linked the missions was known as *El Camino Real,* a route that began in Mexico City and continued up through the northernmost territories of Nueva España, as Mexico was then called. Today these territories are the west and southwest regions of the United States.

Although some of the mission churches were more elaborate than others, their overall architectural style is simple and practical. The churches were built with massive adobe blocks, five feet thick. The blocks couldn't be piled too high because they would topple. At first, the churches were made of wood, with thatching used for the roof. This was changed, however, when flaming arrows during an attack set fire to one of the churches. Adobe became the material for the walls, and clay tiles for the roof. The tiles were fashioned by indigenous workmen who draped the wet clay over their shins to shape the tiles.

The Franciscan missionaries established twelve more missions in California after Father Serra's death in 1784. Today, they are all popular tourist attractions. Father Serra is buried under the altar at the Carmel mission. This was his favorite mission and headquarters, and its church is distinct from the others because of its Moorish architectural style. Yet Father Serra was devoted to all nine of his missions, and some of his biographers estimate that he walked more than 24,000 miles in the fifteen years he served as their president. This distance is greater than that covered during the combined journeys of Marco Polo and Lewis and Clark.

Mission San Carlos Borromeo de Carmelo

Test 19

1 Which one of the following posts did Father Serra <u>not</u> hold in his lifetime?

    A. President of the missions.

    B. Theology professor.

    C. Franciscan monk.

    D. Jesuit missionary.

2 In Father Serra's time, what was the name of the land that today is the state of California?

    F. Baja California.

    G. Nueva España.

    H. El Camino Real.

    I. Alta California.

3 Why did King Carlos III of Spain want missions to extend northward into what is now California?

    A. Because he wanted the Catholic faith to be spread as far as possible.

    B. Because the climate and terrain there would make it easy to colonize.

    C. Because Spain's land there was in danger of being taken by other nations.

    D. Because Mexico's terrain was so dangerous.

4 According to the reading, which one of the following four statements about the mission churches is true?

    F. Their architecture is very similar to that of the cathedrals in Mexico.

    G. They are very tall.

    H. Indigenous builders molded wet clay around their shins to shape the roof tiles.

    I. All of them are identical in architecture and layout.

5 READ THINK EXPLAIN Why do you think the missions are so popular with tourists? Use details and information from the reading to support your answer.

6 READ THINK EXPLAIN Father Serra was only sixteen when he made his commitment to become a priest and seventeen when he was ordained. What personal qualities do you think are necessary for a person that young to make a commitment that is so serious? Do you think that it would be a lot more difficult today for a teenager to make such a decision and commitment? Why or why not?

© Prentice-Hall, Inc.

Nombre: _____ Fecha: _____

1 (A) (B) (C) (D)   **2** (F) (G) (H) (I)   **3** (A) (B) (C) (D)

4 (F) (G) (H) (I)

5

READ
THINK
EXPLAIN

_____
_____
_____
_____
_____
_____

6

READ
THINK
EXPLAIN

_____
_____
_____
_____
_____
_____
_____
_____
_____

STOP

Diario de mi viaje a Perú

Domingo 25 de julio

Estoy en Perú con mis amigos Alberto y Carmen. Estamos en el autobús que va a Cuzco, antigua capital del imperio incaico. Hoy día es una ciudad pequeña y una atracción turística. Berto está sacando cientos de fotos del paisaje. Carmen lo está dibujando. Las montañas son espectaculares. La cordillera de los Andes va del norte al sur de América del Sur.

Miércoles 28 de julio

Es el Día de la Independencia peruana. En esta fecha en 1821, José de San Martín proclamó la independencia de Perú. En Lima, una gran ciudad moderna y capital del país, hay grandes celebraciones hoy. Pero aquí estamos en Machu Picchu, ruinas de una ciudad antigua de los Inca. Es un lugar de mucho interés en las montañas altísimas de Perú. Hiram Bingham, un arqueólogo de Yale University, descubrió Machu Picchu en 1911.

Sábado 31 de julio

Estamos paseando en bote en el lago Titicaca, en la frontera de Perú y Bolivia. Es el lago más grande de estos países y el más alto del mundo. ¡Estamos a más de 3.800 metros de altura! Nuestro bote es un poquito de rojo en un mundo silencioso azul.

Miércoles 4 de agosto

Ahora estamos en un avión pequeño. En la Tierra podemos ver algo muy misterioso: Hay un desierto donde vemos enormes dibujos de animales y figuras geométricas. Estos dibujos se llaman las líneas de Nazca. Miden más de 300 metros y tienen más de dos mil años. ¿Quiénes los dibujaron—y por qué? Es necesario estar en un avión para verlos. ¿Cómo se puede dibujar algo que es tan grande que el artista no puede verlo?

Mañana regresamos a Cuzco y el domingo salimos de Perú. ¡Dos semanas increíbles! Berto tiene sus fotos y Carmen sus dibujos. Pero no soy ni fotógrafo ni artista y voy a comprar tarjetas postales como recuerdos.

1 What is noteworthy about Cuzco?

    A. Even though it is small it is a tourist attraction.

    B. The nearby countryside is mountainous.

    C. It was the capital of the Incan Empire.

    D. It runs all the way from the north to the south of South America.

2 Why is July 28 a noteworthy day in Peru?

    F. It is the equivalent of July 4 in the United States.

    G. In 1821, Lima was proclaimed the capital of the country.

    H. In 1911, Hiram Bingham discovered Machu Picchu.

    I. There are celebrations in Lima.

3 What is noteworthy about Lake Titicaca?

    A. It is the grandest lake in Peru and Bolivia.

    B. It is exceptionally blue and silent with tiny red boats.

    C. It is at a higher altitude than any other lake in the world.

    D. It is the only lake on the border between two countries.

4 Which of the following is <u>not</u> a noteworthy fact about Nazca?

    F. No one knows who created the drawings.

    G. No one knows why the drawings were created.

    H. No one knows how drawings could be made that were so large that the artists could not possibly see what they were drawing.

    I. No one can see the drawings from a plane.

5 En español, escribe una leyenda *(caption)* de 8–10 palabras para cada una de las cuatro fotos.

6 Which one of the places described in the diary would you most like to visit and what would you do there? Explain why that would be your choice.

Test 20

Nombre: _____   Fecha: _____

1 Ⓐ Ⓑ Ⓒ Ⓓ   **2** Ⓕ Ⓖ Ⓗ Ⓘ   **3** Ⓐ Ⓑ Ⓒ Ⓓ

4 Ⓕ Ⓖ Ⓗ Ⓘ

5

READ
THINK
CREATE

_____

_____

_____

_____

_____

_____

_____

_____

6

READ
THINK
EXPLAIN

_____

_____

_____

_____

_____

STOP

Mitos sobre
Cristóbal Colón *y sus viajes*

Cristóbal Colón es posiblemente la figura histórica más famosa en los países de las Américas. Pero esto no quiere decir que lo que generalmente se sabe sobre Colón es verdadero. En realidad, mucha de la información es simplemente una repetición de mitos aceptados por cinco siglos.

Uno de los mitos más populares sobre Colón es que él fue el primero en decir que el mundo es redondo. La verdad es que ésta era una idea generalmente aceptada en la época de Colón. Los matemáticos de la Grecia antigua fueron los primeros en llegar a esta conclusión, y también calcularon con bastante precisión el tamaño del mundo.

Según otro mito, Colón era un navegante brillante. Es más correcto decir que era muy buen marinero, y que conocía los vientos y las corrientes del mar bastante bien. Pero Colón calculaba las distancias horriblemente mal. Pensaba que la Tierra era mucho más pequeña de lo que es. Por eso murió convencido de que en sus cuatro viajes exploró partes de Asia, y no tierras previamente desconocidas. En su primer viaje, cuando llegó a tierra el 12 de octubre de 1492, pensó que estaba en la India, y por eso llamó "indios" a la gente que encontró allí.

Mucha gente en los Estados Unidos piensa que Colón llegó a los Estados Unidos continentales. En realidad, la única parte de los Estados Unidos que él vio o visitó son las Islas Vírgenes y Puerto Rico, que hoy día son territorios estadounidenses. En todos sus viajes, Colón exploró islas en el Atlántico y el Caribe. En su tercer viaje, navegó por la costa de lo que hoy es Venezuela, y en su cuarto, exploró la costa de lo que hoy son Honduras, Nicaragua, Costa Rica y Panamá. Como base para sus cuatro viajes, Colón escogió la isla que él nombró "la Española," donde están hoy día Haití y la República Dominicana. De todos los países en las Américas, la República Dominicana es el único relacionado directamente con Colón—la colonia en Santo Domingo, que hoy es la capital del país, fue gobernada por Colón, sus hermanos y su hijo.

Otro mito sobre Colón es que fue un gobernador justo y bueno. Según este mito, si Colón hizo cosas que hoy día nosotros consideramos brutales, hay que ver estos actos en el contexto de lo que hacía la gente en esa época. Pero en realidad, muchos de los contemporáneos de Colón lo criticaron severamente cuando vieron cómo trataba a la gente bajo su control. Él y sus hermanos torturaban y ejecutaban a sus hombres si no seguían sus órdenes. Tomaban a los indígenas como esclavos para construir sus colonias y para buscar oro. Los indígenas en la Española fueron tratados tan brutalmente que pronto murieron. Cuando Colón llegó a la isla por primera vez, había 250.000 indígenas. Dos años más tarde, quedaban 125.000.

Otro mito muy popular sobre Colón es que murió pobre y en la desgracia. Al contrario, murió bastante rico, con dinero de sus minas americanas, y con sus títulos de Almirante y virrey. Es verdad que los reyes españoles, Fernando e Isabel, no le dieron más poder a Colón cuando vieron que no sabía gobernar y que era muy cruel con sus hombres y con los indígenas. Pero no le quitaron ni su fortuna ni sus honores, y Colón murió en su propio apartamento en Valladolid, España, atendido por su familia y amigos.

Los viajes de Cristóbal Colón, 1492–1503

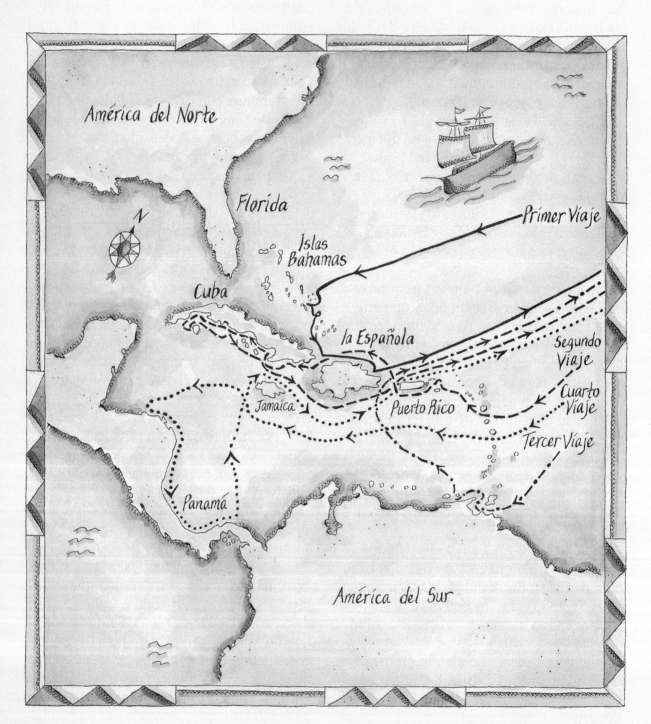

América del Norte

Florida

Islas Bahamas

Cuba

la Española

Jamaica

Puerto Rico

Panamá

América del Sur

Primer Viaje

Segundo Viaje

Cuarto Viaje

Tercer Viaje

1 Which one of the following statements is false?

    A.   Columbus died thinking that he'd reached Asia.

    B.   Columbus neither saw nor visited the United States mainland.

    C.   Columbus made his base on Hispaniola, the island that today is divided into Haiti and the Dominican Republic.

    D.   Columbus was universally admired by his contemporaries.

2 According to the article, what was Columbus's talent as a seaman?

    F.   He could sail by the stars.

    G.   He knew the winds and ocean currents very well.

    H.   He could calculate distances with great accuracy.

    I.   He recognized that the world was round.

3 According to the article, what argument has been made to excuse Columbus's cruelty toward his men and the indigenous people?

    A.   That he had periods of madness in which he was not responsible for his actions.

    B.   That his actions need to be examined in the context of his time.

    C.   That he was provoked and attacked constantly.

    D.   That his cruelty was exaggerated by his enemies.

4 Why did the king and queen of Spain decide not to give Columbus additional power?

    F.   Because he governed poorly and was cruel.

    G.   Because they wanted his brothers to rule.

    H.   Because he wasn't delivering the gold from his mines in the New World.

    I.   Because he was already an admiral and viceroy.

5 **READ THINK EXPLAIN** Nombra algunas cosas que aprendiste del artículo que fueron sorpresas para ti.

6 **READ THINK EXPLAIN** Think carefully about one of the myths about Columbus and explain its appeal. Include in your answer reasons why the myth might have gotten started in the first place as well as why it persists even now.

Nombre: _____ Fecha: _____

1 Ⓐ Ⓑ Ⓒ Ⓓ   **2** Ⓕ Ⓖ Ⓗ Ⓘ   **3** Ⓐ Ⓑ Ⓒ Ⓓ

4 Ⓕ Ⓖ Ⓗ Ⓘ

5

READ
THINK
EXPLAIN

_____
_____
_____
_____
_____
_____

6

READ
THINK
EXPLAIN

_____
_____
_____
_____
_____
_____
_____
_____

STOP

How "Spanish" Is *Spanish* Architecture?

If you were to travel from the southwestern United States to the southern tip of South America, things would look fairly familiar almost every place you visited. Although regional differences would be obvious, you would still be aware of a certain look shared by many communities in the southwestern U.S. and Latin America. In large part, that look can be traced to the architecture of Moorish Spain.

The Moors were North African Arabs who ruled most of the Iberian Peninsula (Spain and Portugal) for nearly 800 years—from the early eighth century until the late fifteenth century. Many elements of Latin American architecture were first introduced to Spain by the Moors during that period.

Patios, for example, became common in cities such as Córdoba and Sevilla beginning in the early eleventh century. Because of widespread political and social unrest during that time, houses were built with heavy doors and thick, fortresslike walls. These walls also helped shield the rooms inside from the sun's heat. The patios, placed in the center of the house and accessible from all first-floor rooms, often had tiled floors. In the center, surrounded by lemon trees and flowers, there was often a pool or a large clay pot filled with cool water. Patios were thus probably the first naturally "air-conditioned" rooms. Throughout Latin America today, as well as in Spain, central patios are still a popular feature of many commercial buildings as well as homes.

Another common element of Latin American architecture is the *balcón,* or *mirador*. In Moorish Spain, homes typically had balconies off the second-floor sleeping areas. These balconies, which often included intricately designed wrought iron railings and grates, overlooked the patio. During the period when Latin America was

being colonized by Spain, balconies became common in Latin America as well. There was, however, a major difference: Most Latin American balconies do not overlook the patio. Instead, they face outward so that people can view the street life of the town.

Buildings in Moorish Spain usually differed from those in northern Europe in another way as well. Although wood was used as a building material, it was not nearly so common as stone, brick, and adobe (heavy clay bricks made of sun-dried earth and straw). Today, builders in Latin America and the southwestern United States continue to use many of these same materials and techniques first introduced by the Moors.

© Prentice-Hall, Inc.

1 When did the Moors conquer Spain?

    A. In the early 500s.

    B. In the early 700s.

    C. In the early 800s.

    D. In the early 1200s.

2 According to the reading, what was the main reason why the doors and walls of Spanish homes were so thick during the time of Moorish rule?

    F. To keep the house cool.

    G. For defense and protection.

    H. To enclose the patio.

    I. Because the Moors were used to living in homes with thick walls.

3 Which of the following is the best English equivalent of *un mirador?*

    A. A door with a mirror in it.

    B. A heavy mirror.

    C. A door onto a patio.

    D. An overlook.

4 Why do architectural features that date to the period of Moorish influence in Spain exist in the southwestern U.S. and Latin America today?

    F. Because it gets very hot in those regions.

    G. Because those regions were conquered by the Moors.

    H. Because those regions were colonized by the Spanish.

    I. Because of political and social unrest in those regions.

5 READ THINK EXPLAIN Based on what you have read, describe what you think might be a modern-day Spaniard's feelings about his or her home and its relation to the neighborhood. How do you think that attitude might differ from the feelings of a homeowner in the United States?

© Prentice-Hall, Inc.

Nombre: _____   Fecha: _____

1 Ⓐ Ⓑ Ⓒ Ⓓ   **2** Ⓕ Ⓖ Ⓗ Ⓘ   **3** Ⓐ Ⓑ Ⓒ Ⓓ

4 Ⓕ Ⓖ Ⓗ Ⓘ

5

READ
THINK
EXPLAIN

_____

_____

_____

_____

_____

_____

_____

_____

_____

_____

STOP

Un desastre en mi dormitorio

Querida Consuelo:

Mi problema es mi hermana, Carmencita. Somos compañeras de cuarto y estoy en una situación terrible. Ella es completamente desordenada. En su lado del dormitorio, la ropa sucia está encima de la cama o está en el suelo. En mi lado del dormitorio, todo está siempre ordenado. Estoy cansada de vivir en un dormitorio como éste. Mi hermana no es muy considerada y no me escucha nunca cuando quiero hablar con ella sobre el problema. ¿Qué debo hacer?

Marisol Sosa
San Pedro de Macorís
República Dominicana

Querida Marisol:

Cuando dos hermanas son compañeras de cuarto, tienen que establecer reglas para mantener buenas relaciones. Si no hay reglas, siempre hay problemas.

Creo que debes hablar con tu hermana en presencia de tus padres. Ellos tienen que comprender qué difícil es la situación para ti. Y tu hermana también necesita tener la oportunidad de expresar sus sentimientos. ¿Cómo pueden tus padres ayudar a resolver el conflicto? Pueden pagarles por hacer los quehaceres de casa. Si Uds. limpian el dormitorio, reciben dinero. Otra solución es que tú puedes ayudar a tu hermana a arreglar su lado del dormitorio. Puedes ayudarla a hacer la cama, pasar la aspiradora, poner la ropa en la cómoda o en el guardarropa y organizar todas las cosas que están en su escritorio. Si tú y tu hermana trabajan juntas, la tarea va a ser más fácil para ella. ¡Buena suerte!

Tu amiga,
Consuelo

© Prentice-Hall, Inc.

1 Why does Marisol write a letter to Consuelo?

    A. She wants to let her know how much she enjoys her column.

    B. She has a problem and needs some advice.

    C. Consuelo has a problem and needs advice from her.

    D. She is responding to a letter written by another reader.

2 What is Marisol's complaint?

    F. She shares a room with her sister, who is completely disorganized.

    G. She shares a room with her sister, who is obsessed with being neat.

    H. She wants to share a room with her sister because they are so much alike.

    I. She wants someone else to share a room with her sister.

3 Which of these suggestions was <u>not</u> made by Consuelo?

    A. She suggests that Marisol's parents consider paying their daughters an allowance for cleaning up their room.

    B. She suggests that Marisol discuss the problem with a counselor.

    C. She suggests that Marisol discuss the problem with her sister and her parents.

    D. She suggests that Marisol offer to help her sister clean up her side of the room.

4 **READ THINK EXPLAIN** Why do you suppose that people write to columnists for advice?

5 **READ THINK CREATE** Write a letter in Spanish similar to the one that Marisol wrote, asking the columnist to help you solve a roommate problem that you have not been able to solve on your own. Remember to use the same format for your letter.

Nombre: _____ Fecha: _____

1 Ⓐ Ⓑ Ⓒ Ⓓ **2** Ⓕ Ⓖ Ⓗ Ⓘ **3** Ⓐ Ⓑ Ⓒ Ⓓ

4

READ
THINK
EXPLAIN

_____
_____
_____
_____

5

READ
THINK
CREATE

_____
_____
_____
_____
_____
_____
_____
_____
_____
_____
_____
_____

STOP

La Casa de los Azulejos

En Nueva España, como se llamaba México en el siglo XVII, había un joven muy rico. Este joven, quien se llamaba Luis, siempre tenía conflictos con su padre porque le encantaba gastar su dinero en lujos extravagantes.

"¡Con muchos sacrificios gané nuestra fortuna, y ahora tú vas a terminar con ella!" le decía su padre a Luis. "Por favor, hijo, piensa en lo que haces!" Pero Luis no pensaba en nada más que gastar dinero y llamar la atención de todos con sus lujos.

La fama de Luis y cómo gastaba la fortuna de su padre llegó a los oídos del virrey (el representante del rey español en Nueva España) quien dijo con mucho sarcasmo: "Ése no hará nunca casa de azulejos." Este comentario quería decir que Luis nunca haría nada bueno con su dinero. Para recuperar su honor, Luis compró una hermosa mansión en el centro de la ciudad. Y para indicar que el virrey no tenía razón, Luis decoró su mansión con brillantes azulejos que tenían bellos dibujos en azul, blanco y amarillo. Así, dice la tradición popular, fue cómo originó la Casa de los Azulejos.

Se dice también que muchos años después, Luis compró muebles elegantes para la casa y organizó una fiesta en honor de sus padres. Todos lo pasaban bien en el baile cuando don Luis notó que un reloj muy caro no estaba en su lugar. Entonces los músicos ya no tocaron y Luis dijo a los invitados:

"Alguien me robó un reloj de oro y piedras preciosas que me regaló el rey. Miren, el reloj

estaba allí, al lado de la ventana. Pero no importa porque a las doce de la noche, el reloj tocará música que se oirá en toda la sala. Así vamos a saber quién es el ladrón."

Para darle al ladrón la oportunidad de devolver el reloj, apagaron las luces.

Cuando volvieron a encenderlas, todos vieron que el reloj estaba otra vez en su lugar. Entonces la fiesta continuó.

Ninguno de los invitados sabía que a las doce de la noche, ¡el reloj no iba a tocar ninguna música! Todo fue una ingeniosa idea de don Luis para recuperar su reloj.

1 Where does this story take place?

    A. In Spain.

    B. In New Mexico.

    C. In Mexico.

    D. In Azulejos.

2 Why was Luis's father so unhappy with him?

    F. Because Luis was wasting the family fortune.

    G. Because Luis was always breaking the law.

    H. Because Luis was more famous than he was.

    I. Because Luis didn't buy anything for his father.

3 How did Luis react to the viceroy's negative comment about him?

    A. He laughed about it.

    B. He became angry and confronted him about it.

    C. He was offended and decided to try to rebuild his reputation.

    D. He paid no attention to it.

4 What is the origin of the Casa de los Azulejos?

    F. It's the mansion that the king gave Luis.

    G. It's the mansion that Luis bought and decorated with blue, white, and yellow tiles.

    H. It's the mansion that Luis bought from his father.

    I. It's the mansion that Luis's father bought.

5 READ THINK EXPLAIN ¿Por qué crees que el dinero es la causa de muchos conflictos entre padres e hijos? ¿Cómo reaccionan tus padres cuando no piensas antes de gastar dinero?

Nombre: _____   Fecha: _____

1 Ⓐ   Ⓑ   Ⓒ   Ⓓ   **2** Ⓕ   Ⓖ   Ⓗ   Ⓘ   **3** Ⓐ   Ⓑ   Ⓒ   Ⓓ

4 Ⓕ   Ⓖ   Ⓗ   Ⓘ

5

READ
THINK
EXPLAIN

_____

_____

_____

_____

_____

_____

STOP

How Florida *Got Its* Oranges

Florida has long been a world leader in orange and orange juice production, currently ranking second only to Brazil. Every year, over 11 million tons of oranges are harvested in the United States, and Florida alone accounts for approximately 75 percent of that harvest.

Almost all Florida oranges—nearly 94 percent in 1998—are processed into orange juice. Most of this juice becomes frozen concentrate, but some is packaged in cartons, bottles, and cans. In fact, frozen concentrated orange juice was invented in 1945 by scientists at the Florida Department of Citrus. Three years later, the department gave the patent for the process to the U.S. government, thereby helping to launch the entire frozen food industry.

But oranges had been making history in Florida long before the twentieth century. The bumper crops and high-tech agricultural methods that produce them are the current phase of a history that began thousands of years ago, across many continents.

Oranges are believed to have originated in China about 4,000 years ago. From there, they spread to Southeast Asia, India, Africa, and the Middle East. By the eighth century, Arab traders and conquerors had introduced oranges to Spain and Portugal. They flourished in the warm, sunny regions

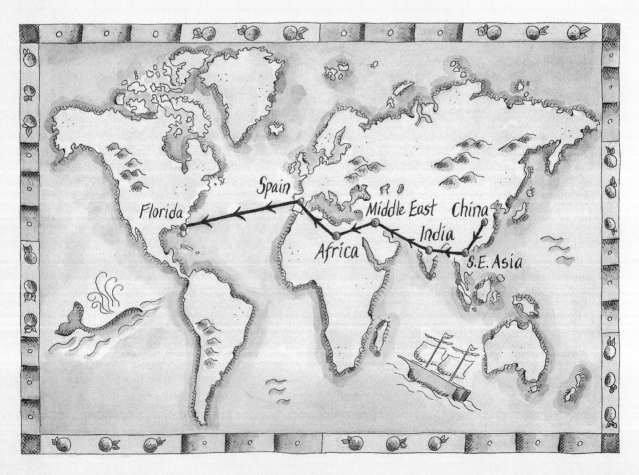

of these countries, which continue to be leaders in orange production in the world today. Valencia, a variety of orange now grown in Florida, takes its name from a region in Spain.

The Americas got their first oranges and other citrus fruits in 1493, when Christopher Columbus brought them to Haiti and the Caribbean on his second voyage. These fruits were prized by sailors as a means of preventing scurvy, a disease caused when a diet lacks ascorbic acid, or vitamin C, which is contained in fresh produce. During the Age of Exploration, Portuguese, Spanish, Dutch, and Arab sailors planted citrus fruits along all their trade routes to combat this disease, which afflicted them during long sea voyages.

In time, Spanish law came to require that each sailor on a Spanish ship bound for the Americas carry 100 citrus seeds with him. So it was that in 1513, when Ponce de León first landed in Florida, he and his expedition came with bundles of seeds to plant everywhere they explored. In 1565, Pedro Menéndez de Avilés brought young orange trees to St. Augustine.

By 1820, St. Augustine was producing more than two million oranges every year. When a freeze in 1835 killed the town's groves, citrus growers went inland to the west or south. In the mid-1870s, citrus growers in central Florida imported 200 million oranges, trees, and cuttings from Mediterranean Europe and the West Indies. The future for oranges in Florida looked bright by 1885, when the state had about 60 varieties of oranges under cultivation and produced 600,000 boxes of them. But freezing weather, which could strike at any time, continued to be a troubling factor.

In 1886, a Chinese immigrant named Lue Gim Gong came to the rescue. Having moved from Massachusetts to DeLand to regain his health, he set out to develop an orange that could survive cold temperatures. By 1888, Gong had accomplished both of his goals—his health was better and his orange, which is still grown in the Indian River region, received an award from the United States Department of Agriculture. By 1894, Florida orange production had reached 5 million boxes per year.

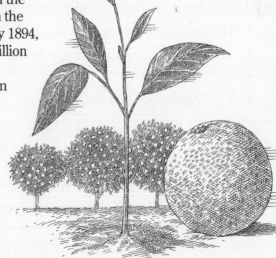

Today, freezing weather is still a problem for orange growers in Florida. This will always be the case, or at least until human beings figure out how to control the weather. But thanks to the continuing efforts of scientists to develop hardier varieties of oranges, Florida stands to maintain its position as a world leader in oranges and orange juice production for a long time to come.

Test 25

1 According to the article, what happens to most Florida oranges?

    A. They are shipped to other countries.

    B. They are sold by the Florida Department of Citrus.

    C. They are believed to have originated in China.

    D. They are used to make orange juice.

2 What did Spanish law require of sailors on ships bound for the New World?

    F. That they sign up for at least five years of service.

    G. That each of them carry 100 citrus seeds to plant.

    H. That they try to find a cure for scurvy.

    I. That they claim land for Spain.

3 According to the article, why did citrus growers move inland to central Florida to plant their groves?

    A. Because there were too many orange trees in St. Augustine.

    B. Because they needed more land for all the imported varieties of oranges.

    C. To avoid freezing weather.

    D. Because Lue Gim Gong developed an orange that grew especially well there.

4 Nombra la cosa más interesante que aprendiste de este artículo.

5 How would you rank the following in terms of their influence on the development of orange production in Florida:

- The pre-eighth-century Arab traders and conquerors
- The sailors of the Age of Exploration
- Lue Gim Gong
- The Florida Department of Citrus

Explain your rankings.

Nombre: _____   Fecha: _____

1 Ⓐ Ⓑ Ⓒ Ⓓ   **2** Ⓕ Ⓖ Ⓗ Ⓘ   **3** Ⓐ Ⓑ Ⓒ Ⓓ

4

READ
THINK
EXPLAIN

_____

_____

_____

_____

_____

_____

5

READ
THINK
EXPLAIN

_____

_____

_____

_____

_____

_____

_____

_____

STOP

Test 26

Health

PASO A PASO 1	PASO A PASO 2	PASO A PASO 3
Chapter 9	Chapter 9	

Los maratones

El maratón es la más larga de todas las carreras: 42.2 kilómetros (un poco más de 26 millas). Esa distancia es la que hay aproximadamente entre la ciudad griega de Maratón y Atenas, la capital de Grecia. El maratón toma su nombre del acto legendario de un soldado griego en el año 490 antes de Cristo. Según la tradición, el soldado corrió sin descanso y a máxima velocidad de Maratón a Atenas para anunciar la victoria de Grecia contra Persia en la batalla de Maratón. En aquel tiempo, Persia (que hoy día es el país de Irán) quería invadir Grecia para hacerla parte del imperio persa. Según la tradición, después de llegar a Atenas, el soldado griego anunció la victoria y murió inmediatamente.

Esta leyenda inspiró a los organizadores de los Juegos Olímpicos modernos. Estos juegos en 1896 fueron los primeros desde la antigüedad y se celebraron, apropiadamente, en Grecia. Para conmemorar al soldado griego legendario, los organizadores incluyeron una carrera entre las ciudades de Atenas y Maratón. El maratón todavía es uno de los eventos más populares de los Juegos Olímpicos modernos.

Hoy día muchas ciudades también organizan maratones todos los años, y atletas de todos los países participan en ellos. Tres de los maratones urbanos más famosos son

Khalid Khannouchi, ganador del maratón de Chicago en 1999

los de Boston, de Chicago y de Nueva York. El maratón de Boston, establecido en 1897, es el más antiguo de los maratones urbanos. El maratón de Nueva York, que se estableció en 1970, es el más grande, con más de 10.000 participantes. En 1973 los maratones admitieron mujeres por primera vez.

Khalid Khannouchi tiene el récord mundial de 2 horas, 5 minutos, 42 segundos. Fue obtenido en el maratón de Chicago en 1999. Khannouchi nació en Marruecos en el norte de África, pero está en el proceso de hacerse ciudadano de los Estados Unidos.

El año de 1999 también fue muy importante para Adriana Fernández de México, quien ganó el maratón de Nueva York en la división de las mujeres. Fue la primera vez que una mexicana ganó un maratón internacional. Su tiempo fue 2 horas, 25 minutos, 6 segundos.

Adriana Fernández, ganadora del maratón de Nueva York en 1999

1 Which one of the following statements is false?

    A.   The marathon is named after a Greek soldier.

    B.   The marathon is an event in the modern Olympic Games.

    C.   Marathons are held annually in many cities around the world.

    D.   International athletes compete in marathons.

2 According to the article, why did the soldier die after giving the news that the Greeks had defeated the Persians?

    F.   Because he received a mortal blow after he got to Athens.

    G.   Because there were orders to kill him after he gave his message.

    H.   Because he was exhausted from running.

    I.   Because he was wounded when he began running.

3 Why was 1999 an important year for marathons?

    A.   Because it was the first time a woman had ever won a marathon.

    B.   Because a new world record was set.

    C.   Because it was the first time a marathon was won by someone from Morocco.

    D.   Because there were more urban marathons than ever before.

4 **READ THINK EXPLAIN** ¿Por qué crees que los maratones urbanos son populares?

5 **READ THINK EXPLAIN** Do you think that having a positive mindset is as important as good physical training for an athlete preparing to compete? Explain your answer.

Nombre: _____   Fecha: _____

1 Ⓐ Ⓑ Ⓒ Ⓓ   **2** Ⓕ Ⓖ Ⓗ Ⓘ   **3** Ⓐ Ⓑ Ⓒ Ⓓ

4

READ
THINK
EXPLAIN

_____

_____

_____

_____

_____

5

READ
THINK
EXPLAIN

_____

_____

_____

_____

_____

_____

_____

_____

STOP

Sara María Dolores Sánchez Papillón

Adaptado de un poema de Elizabeth Millán

Hace más de una semana que tiene sarampión
Sara María Dolores Sánchez Papillón.
Sus amigas no la pueden ver, ni ella las puede visitar—
ellas por miedo del sarampión y Sara por no contagiar.
5 ¡Pobrecita! Está aburridísima.
(Pero el médico dice que pronto va a estar sanísima.)
Ella está tan cansada—
¡prefiere estudiar que no hacer nada!
No mira la televisión
10 y no le gusta la música.
¡Necesita una solución—
buena y rapidísima!
Decide una mañana
mirar por la ventana
15 para ver lo que pasa
fuera de su casa.
¡Es casi increíble lo que ve Sara!
Es el circo de don Enrique Sierra—
¡el más fabuloso de la Tierra!

20 ¡Qué espectáculo! ¡Qué divertido!
    Trapecistas, tigres, elefantes,
    acróbatas, osos y leones gigantes.
    Hay dos chimpancés que saben cantar
    y cinco hipopótamos que pueden patinar.
25 ¡Y llegan tres osos que les enseñan a bailar!
    Hay perros, rinocerontes y muchos payasos—
    Que caminan sonriendo y dándose abrazos.
    A Sara le encanta muchísimo la atracción
    y pronto se olvida del sarampión.
30 Pero un momento . . .
    ¿Qué es esto? ¿Y qué pasa?
    El circo sube. ¿Es posible? ¡Todos suben a su casa!
    Y entran todos en su dormitorio:
    Los chimpancés y los hipopótamos con su repertorio,
35 los perros, los rinocerontes y los elefantes,
    ¡y ya entran los leones gigantes!
    Los osos suben y bailan sobre la cama
    y los acróbatas y trapecistas completan el drama.
    ¡Tanto ruido! ¡Tanta confusión!
40 (Sara ni ve a los payasos subir en camión.)
    —¿Qué hago? ¿Qué hago?—dice la pobre.
    —¿Por qué no bajan todos por la misma escalera
    y me dejan tranquila?—por fin llora Sara.
    Pero nadie la escucha ni ve cuando en el dormitorio
45 entra el doctor don Félix Retiborio.
    El médico mira a todos y por fin proclama:
    —Nadie puede salir hasta la próxima semana.
    ¡Gracias al sarampión
    de Sara María Dolores Sánchez Papillón!

1 Why can't anyone come to see Sara?

    A.   Because the doctor is coming.

    B.   Because she's going to the circus.

    C.   Because she prefers to study.

    D.   Because she has the measles.

2 How does Sara feel at the beginning of the poem?

    F.   Bored to death.

    G.   Afraid.

    H.   Tired of watching TV.

    I.   Really healthy.

3 Beginning at line 30, how does Sara feel about the circus animals, acrobats, and clowns?

    A.   She wishes they would use the stairs.

    B.   She loves all the noise and confusion.

    C.   She is afraid that none of them are having fun.

    D.   She wishes they'd go away and leave her alone.

4 At the end of the poem, why can't anyone leave?

    F.   Because the doctor is standing in the doorway.

    G.   Because they've been exposed to measles and are now contagious.

    H.   Because Sara's measles won't be gone until next week.

    I.   Because they are all in one another's way.

5 READ THINK EXPLAIN   Cuando una persona tiene sarampión, a menudo tiene mucha fiebre también. Esto puede causar a la persona a tener pesadillas *(nightmares)*. ¿Crees que el poema describe una pesadilla o no? ¿Por qué crees eso?

6 READ THINK EXPLAIN   Escoge por lo menos dos líneas del poema y cámbialas. No olvides la rima ni el metro.

Test 27

Nombre: _____   Fecha: _____

1 Ⓐ Ⓑ Ⓒ Ⓓ   **2** Ⓕ Ⓖ Ⓗ Ⓘ   **3** Ⓐ Ⓑ Ⓒ Ⓓ

4 Ⓕ Ⓖ Ⓗ Ⓘ

5

READ
THINK
EXPLAIN

_____
_____
_____
_____
_____
_____

6

READ
THINK
EXPLAIN

_____
_____
_____
_____
_____
_____
_____
_____

STOP

Would You Like to Be a Volunteer?

Have you ever considered using your Spanish-language skills to improve or even save someone's life? Would it interest you to volunteer someday for an organization located in one of the Spanish-speaking countries that you've studied? Even if you've never thought about these questions, read on. You might have an answer by the end of this article that could make a wonderful, lasting difference in someone else's life—and your own!

Casa Alianza is a nonprofit organization whose goal is to rehabilitate and defend homeless children in Guatemala, Honduras, Mexico, and Nicaragua. Founded in Guatemala in 1981, Casa Alianza's programs and services support and care for nearly 4,000 children annually, many of them civil-war orphans, victims of abuse or neglect, or living in poverty. The organization's motto is: *"Ningún niño o niña debería vivir en la calle."*

The organization's Web site not only provides detailed information about its volunteer programs but also personal histories about some of the children who have benefited from Casa Alianza. These first-person accounts of their lives before and after Casa Alianza document the organization's success in redirecting the lives of the children they serve.

Volunteers may serve in many areas, but perhaps the most rewarding experience is working directly with a homeless child in a country of your choice. To do so, you must be fluent in Spanish, have experience in education, psychology, teaching, or another area that deals with children, and make a commitment to serve for six months to one year and to adhere to the principles that are the foundation of the program.

Potential volunteers must submit a résumé, three letters of recommendation, and a personal letter in Spanish telling why they would like to volunteer, what they can offer the children, what they would learn from them, and in which country they would prefer to serve. After the most appropriate candidates have been identified, information is forwarded to the country of choice. Every effort is made to match candidates with their first choice. However, if this is not possible, an alternate location is suggested.

Although the qualifications listed earlier are important, the most important ones have not been mentioned. Because the children served by Casa Alianza come from environments where they have been mistreated, they often find it difficult to confide in adults. As a result, volunteers must be able to gain their confidence and convince them that they can have better lives. Dedication and a genuine concern for the children are also essential for anyone interested in becoming a volunteer for this organization.

1 What is Casa Alianza?

    A. A restaurant that serves homeless people.

    B. An organization dedicated to serving homeless children.

    C. A home for volunteers in Mexico and Central America.

    D. A Web site about volunteer organizations.

2 What makes Casa Alianza's Web site unique?

    F. It contains firsthand information from children who have participated in the program.

    G. It gives applicants an opportunity to interact with children from the program.

    H. It gives detailed information about Guatemala, Honduras, Mexico, and Nicaragua.

    I. It matches candidates with the countries they have selected.

3 What are some of the qualifications for Casa Alianza volunteers?

    A. They must have studied Spanish for at least six months.

    B. They must be residents of one of the sponsor countries.

    C. They must be fluent in Spanish and have experience in working with children.

    D. They must write a personal history for the Web site.

4 READ THINK EXPLAIN

Why do you think Casa Alianza is located in Guatemala, Honduras, Mexico, and Nicaragua?

5 READ THINK CREATE

Imagine that you would like to be a Casa Alianza volunteer. Write a short letter in Spanish telling why you want to be a volunteer. Use details and information from the reading in your answer.

Nombre: _____ Fecha: _____

1 Ⓐ Ⓑ Ⓒ Ⓓ   **2** Ⓕ Ⓖ Ⓗ Ⓘ   **3** Ⓐ Ⓑ Ⓒ Ⓓ

4

READ
THINK
EXPLAIN

_____

_____

_____

_____

5

READ
THINK
CREATE

_____

_____

_____

_____

_____

_____

_____

_____

_____

_____

_____

STOP

Test 29

Community and Volunteerism

PASO A PASO 1	PASO A PASO 2	PASO A PASO 3
Chapter 10	Chapter 11	Chapter 7

¡Bienvenidos *a la calle* Olvera!

Si vas a Los Ángeles, tienes que visitar la calle Olvera, una cuadra que está en el centro antiguo de la ciudad y que tiene una atmósfera totalmente mexicana. En el año 1930, esta calle se transformó en un mercado mexicano donde se puede comprar toda clase de productos mexicanos y comer platos mexicanos auténticos. Los fines de semana muchas personas comen en los restaurantes y los mariachis tocan música en la plaza cerca de esta calle.

La calle Olvera lleva el nombre de Agustín Olvera, quien vivió enfrente de la plaza en el siglo XIX y fue uno de los primeros oficiales de la ciudad. Es una de las calles más antiguas de la ciudad y tiene mucho interés histórico. Allí están muchos de los sitios más antiguos como Casa Pelanconi, donde está situado Café La Golondrina, el primer restaurante en Los Ángeles que sirvió comida mexicana auténtica.

Si estás en la calle Olvera en un día de fiesta mexicano, puedes ver tradiciones y ceremonias muy importantes de la cultura mexicana. Se celebran algunos de los días de fiesta mexicanos más populares en la plaza cerca de la calle Olvera. El Cinco de Mayo conmemora la victoria de los soldados mexicanos sobre los soldados franceses en Puebla en 1862. El 16 de septiembre se celebra el Día de la Independencia de México porque ése fue el día en 1810 en que los mexicanos empezaron a luchar por su independencia de España. El dos de noviembre se celebra el Día de los Muertos, el día en que las familias mexicanas van a los cementerios para conmemorar a sus familiares muertos. Cada noche entre el 16 y el 24 de diciembre se celebran las posadas, una fiesta que conmemora los nueve días cuando la Virgen María y San José buscaron un lugar para quedarse hasta la llegada del Niño Jesús.

Hoy día la calle Olvera forma parte del Monumento Histórico del Pueblo de Los Ángeles. Si vas allí, vas a tener una experiencia muy interesante. Casi dos millones de personas visitan la calle Olvera cada año para participar en las actividades culturales, cenar en los restaurantes y aprender más sobre la historia de Los Ángeles.

1 In the article, three of the following are mentioned as ways in which Olvera Street resembles a community in Mexico. Which one is not mentioned?

    A.   Vendors sell Mexican products.

    B.   Restaurants serve authentic Mexican food.

    C.   Mariachis provide entertainment.

    D.   Visitors bargain for the products they would like to buy.

2 Three of the following statements are false. Which one is true?

    F.   Olvera Street was named in honor of Agustín Olvera, Los Angeles County's first official.

    G.   Olvera Street is the oldest street in Los Angeles.

    H.   Olvera Street is the site of some of the oldest buildings in Los Angeles.

    I.   Olvera Street is located just outside of Los Angeles.

3 Which of the following statements best describes how the celebration of *las posadas* differs from the other celebrations mentioned?

    A.   It takes place over a period of several days and commemorates a religious event.

    B.   It commemorates a famous event in Mexican history.

    C.   It commemorates a famous tradition celebrated in Mexico.

    D.   It takes place only once a year.

4 **READ THINK EXPLAIN** ¿Qué impacto crees que las comunidades diversas de los Estados Unidos tienen sobre lo que llamamos "la cultura estadounidense"? Usa detalles e información del artículo en tu respuesta.

5 **READ THINK EXPLAIN** Piensa en un lugar en tu comunidad o en otra comunidad que es similar a la calle Olvera. ¿Qué hacen los habitantes de esa comunidad para celebrar su cultura?

Nombre: _____   Fecha: _____

1 Ⓐ Ⓑ Ⓒ Ⓓ   **2** Ⓕ Ⓖ Ⓗ Ⓘ   **3** Ⓐ Ⓑ Ⓒ Ⓓ

4

READ
THINK
EXPLAIN

_____

_____

_____

_____

_____

_____

5

READ
THINK
EXPLAIN

_____

_____

_____

_____

_____

_____

_____

_____

_____

_____

STOP

Mary McLeod Bethune

En 1904, una joven profesora afroamericana llegó a Daytona Beach, Florida. Tenía el sueño de fundar una escuela para enseñar a jóvenes afroamericanas las habilidades que necesitaban para obtener empleos. Su nombre era Mary McLeod Bethune, y su mejor cualidad era su determinación. Encontró una pequeña casa y dio un depósito de $1.50 para obtenerla. Con sólo cinco estudiantes, Bethune fundó su escuela, Daytona Normal and Industrial Institute for Girls.

Al principio, el éxito parecía imposible. En aquel tiempo, en el sur de los Estados Unidos, los estudiantes blancos y negros no podían ir a la misma escuela. Era ilegal. Las escuelas para los estudiantes negros recibían poco dinero, y por eso Bethune y sus estudiantes se dedicaron a hacer y vender tartas todos los días para ganar dinero. Bethune también recogía cosas de la basura de los hoteles para turistas y de la basura de la ciudad. Bethune y sus estudiantes limpiaban, reparaban y usaban lo que encontraban.

Bethune también pidió ayuda a la gente rica de Daytona. James B. Gamble, de la corporación Procter and Gamble, admiraba mucho la determinación de Bethune. Decidió donar dinero a su escuela, y sirvió como uno de sus directores. Las acciones de Gamble inspiraron a otros. Con su ayuda, Bethune construyó una escuela apropiada para sus estudiantes.

En 1923, la escuela de Bethune se juntó con una escuela que era sólo para hombres. Esta nueva escuela se llamó Bethune-Cookman College.

Más tarde, Mary McLeod Bethune formó el National Council of Negro Women, dirigió otras organizaciones y fue consejera a dos presidentes de

Bethune enfrente de White Hall en Bethune-Cookman College, Daytona Beach, Florida, 1943

los Estados Unidos. En 1954, después de la decisión de la Corte Suprema sobre *Brown v. Board of Education of Topeka,* Bethune expresó las ideas que guiaron su vida:

"Bajo la Constitución, no puede haber democracia dividida, ... ni un país medio libre. Por eso, no puede haber discriminación, ni segregación, ni separación de algunos ciudadanos de los derechos que tienen todos los ciudadanos."

Dra. Mary McLeod Bethune

1 What was Bethune's goal in creating a school for African American girls?

    A.   To teach them general school subjects.

    B.   To prove that African Americans valued education.

    C.   To train them to be social and political advocates for African Americans.

    D.   To teach them job skills.

2 According to the article, why would it have been impossible for Bethune to start a school that accepted both black and white children?

    F.   Because white people wouldn't send their children there anyway.

    G.   Because in some states it was against the law for students of both races to attend the same school.

    H.   Because she didn't have funds to build a big enough school.

    I.   Because her teaching staff refused to teach mixed-race classes.

3 What did Bethune and her students do to raise money for the school?

    A.   They went door to door selling things other people had thrown away.

    B.   They wrote to churches and other community organizations.

    C.   They baked and sold pies.

    D.   They formed other organizations to help African Americans.

4 Which one of the following did Bethune <u>not</u> do later in life?

    F.   Formed the National Council of Negro Women.

    G.   Served as United States ambassador to several countries.

    H.   Led several organizations.

    I.   Advised Presidents.

5 | READ THINK EXPLAIN | Lee de nuevo lo que dice Bethune sobre la democracia y la libertad. Nombra dos derechos que, bajo la Constitución, tienen todos los ciudadanos.

6 | READ THINK EXPLAIN | What other qualities, besides determination, do you think Mary McLeod Bethune must have had to accomplish what she did? Explain your answer.

Nombre: _____ Fecha: _____

1 Ⓐ Ⓑ Ⓒ Ⓓ   **2** Ⓕ Ⓖ Ⓗ Ⓘ   **3** Ⓐ Ⓑ Ⓒ Ⓓ

4 Ⓕ Ⓖ Ⓗ Ⓘ

5

READ
THINK
EXPLAIN

_____

_____

_____

_____

_____

_____

6

READ
THINK
EXPLAIN

_____

_____

_____

_____

_____

_____

_____

_____

_____

_____

STOP

Spanish-Language Television *in the United States*

Spanish-language television was first broadcast in the United States in New York City and San Antonio in the mid-1940s, at approximately the same time as English-language television. The Spanish-language programs were shown in various time slots on certain English-language channels. The first full-fledged Spanish-language station, KCOR-TV in San Antonio, began broadcasting in 1955. Among its early shows was *Buscando estrellas,* a talent show that brought young entertainers from Mexico to Texas.

Today there is a large, well-established audience for Spanish-language broadcasting in the United States. Viewers can enjoy *telenovelas* and other entertainment shows from Mexico, Argentina, Venezuela, and Spain, as well as from such U.S. cities as New York and Miami. International sports events are beamed by satellite from around the globe, with commentary and play-by-play coverage in Spanish.

Because Hispanic populations in this country represent many different countries and cultures, it has been a challenge to create programs that will appeal to this diverse market. One major success was a *telenovela* entitled *Angélica, mi vida,* produced in Puerto Rico in the 1980s. Its subplots dealt with love, tragedy, and power among families of Puerto Rican, Cuban, and Mexican origin.

Today's programs include the most-watched talk show in the world, Miami-based *Cristina,* and the longest-running show on Spanish-language television, *Sábado gigante,* which began broadcasting from Miami in 1986. Cuban-born Cristina Saralegui, who hosts her own show, engages her guests and audiences in lively debates on topical issues. *Sábado gigante* is hosted by Chilean-born Mario Kreutzberger, who uses the pseudonym Don Francisco on his show, which features celebrity guests, contests, games, comedy, and interviews on topics of interest to the Hispanic community. Popular programs originating from outside the U.S. include *El show de Chespirito* (Mexico), *Informe semanal* (Spain), and *Sábados felices* (Colombia).

English-language shows are also shown on Spanish-language TV channels, usually dubbed into Spanish. Among the longest-running of these are cartoon series, such as *The Pink Panther (La Pantera rosa)* and *Spiderman (El Hombre araña).*

1 Where were the first full-time, regularly scheduled U.S. Spanish-language television programs broadcast from?

    A.   Florida.

    B.   Mexico.

    C.   New York.

    D.   Texas.

2 Why was *Buscando estrellas* an appropriate name for that particular show?

    F.   Because it highlighted Mexican entertainers.

    G.   Because it was trying to find up-and-coming young entertainers.

    H.   Because it was one of the first shows on KCOR-TV.

    I.   Because it was broadcast regularly.

3 What do Cristina Saralegui and Mario Kreutzberger have in common?

    A.   They were both born in South America.

    B.   They both broadcast from Florida.

    C.   They both use pseudonyms.

    D.   Neither of them invites audience participation.

4 Which one of the following statements is <u>not</u> true?

    F.   Cultural differences can make programming for Spanish-speaking audiences difficult.

    G.   Some of the most popular Spanish-language programs are broadcast from Miami.

    H.   *Telenovelas* are filmed in Puerto Rico with actors from many countries.

    I.   Most English-language programs are broadcast on Spanish-language television using a Spanish soundtrack.

5 Based on the article, in what ways would you say that Spanish-language and English-language television programs are similar? In what ways are they different?

Test 31

1 Ⓐ Ⓑ Ⓒ Ⓓ   **2** Ⓕ Ⓖ Ⓗ Ⓘ   **3** Ⓐ Ⓑ Ⓒ Ⓓ

4 Ⓕ Ⓖ Ⓗ Ⓘ

5

READ
THINK
EXPLAIN

_____

_____

_____

_____

_____

_____

STOP

Música latina
en la televisión

¿Te gusta ver los videos musicales de Ricky Martin, Marc Anthony, Gloria Estefan, Jennifer Lopez y otros artistas latinos? Pues, la siguiente información te va a interesar.

MTV Latino es un canal de televisión por cable que empezó en 1993 y que da programas musicales las 24 horas del día. Es el canal favorito del 50 por ciento de los jóvenes latinos en los Estados Unidos. A ellos les fascina porque en este canal dan toda clase de videos musicales, noticias sobre música, artistas, bandas, conciertos y películas, y entrevistas con los artistas más populares. También los jóvenes pueden llamar por teléfono y pedir su video favorito.

Ricky Martin canta y baila al ritmo latino.

Gloria Estefan canta con Justin Timberlake y JC Chasez de *NSync.

MTV en Telemundo también da programas musicales para los jóvenes. Este programa de televisión por cable, que empezó en septiembre de 1999, es una colaboración entre Telemundo, una de las compañías de programación en español más grandes, y MTV Latinoamérica. Los viernes a las once y media de la noche y los sábados a las once de la noche, los jóvenes pueden ver los diez videos musicales más populares de la semana y también los bailes más populares del mundo latino.

1 According to the reading, which of the following is <u>not</u> one of the reasons why teens watch *MTV Latino?*

    A.   It offers a variety of musical programming.

    B.   It presents news about and interviews with their favorite recording artists.

    C.   It allows them to call in and request their favorite videos.

    D.   It doesn't cost anything to receive it.

2 How does *MTV en Telemundo* differ from *MTV Latino?*

    F.   It offers musical programming, but not on a 24-hour basis.

    G.   It's available on cable television.

    H.   It's older than *MTV Latino.*

    I.   It presents music videos.

3 READ THINK EXPLAIN   ¿Por qué crees que la música latina es tan popular entre los jóvenes de los Estados Unidos?

Nombre: _____   Fecha: _____

1 Ⓐ Ⓑ Ⓒ Ⓓ   **2** Ⓕ Ⓖ Ⓗ Ⓘ

3

READ
THINK
EXPLAIN

_____
_____
_____
_____
_____
_____

STOP

Ray Suarez

Entre los reporteros de televisión y radio más respetados de los Estados Unidos, Ray Suarez, nacido en 1957, es bastante joven. Pero hace veinte años que Suarez es reportero, y en ese tiempo ha trabajado en muchas de las principales ciudades del mundo.

Como reportero, Suarez es famoso por sus entrevistas de personas famosas y su análisis de eventos con impacto histórico. En su trabajo en programas de *talk radio,* Suarez también es excepcional por su talento especial para conversar con personas "ordinarias" sobre cosas que son importantes para ellos. Su excelente trabajo le ha ganado muchos premios y honores. Entre los más importantes está el premio 1993/94 Alfred I. DuPont-Columbia University Silver Baton. Suarez ganó este premio por su programa de radio en NPR (National Public Radio), *Talk of the Nation,* que se transmitió desde Sudáfrica cuando, por primera vez, las elecciones en ese país incluyeron personas de todas las razas.

Otro honor ocurrió en octubre de 1999, cuando Suarez llegó a ser *senior correspondent* en el prestigioso programa, *The NewsHour with Jim Lehrer.* Este programa de noticias de televisión se transmite todas las noches de lunes a viernes por medio de PBS (Public Broadcasting System). Tiene un público de más de 3 millones de personas en todos los Estados Unidos.

Suarez nació Rafael Ángel Suarez, Jr. en Brooklyn, New York, de padres puertorriqueños. Estudió en New York University, donde su especialidad fue la historia africana. También estudió en la universidad de Chicago, donde recibió su diploma de maestro en artes en estudios urbanos.

Suarez ha trabajado en Washington, D.C., Los Ángeles, Nueva York, Roma y Londres. También trabajó por siete años en Chicago, donde ayudó a fundar la organización Chicago Association of Hispanic Journalists. Fue voluntario con la YMCA de Chicago para ayudar a jóvenes pandilleros a abandonar su vida de crimen y violencia como miembros de pandillas, y empezar una vida nueva.

Además de su trabajo en *The NewsHour with Jim Lehrer,* Suarez escribe artículos y ensayos sobre temas políticos y sociales para varias revistas. En 1999, se publicó su libro, *The Old Neighborhood: What We Lost in the Great Suburban Migration, 1966-1999.* En este libro, Suarez examina por qué ya no existe un espíritu de comunidad en las grandes ciudades de los Estados Unidos. Habla francamente de problemas entre las razas en estas ciudades, y de cómo estos problemas contribuyeron a la migración de la gente blanca a los suburbios.

Una de las observaciones más interesantes de Suarez en *The Old Neighborhood* es sobre los latinos. Dice que los latinos en las grandes ciudades de los Estados Unidos son "invisibles" para los americanos, aunque están en todas partes haciendo los trabajos difíciles y necesarios para mejorar la vida de todos.

Algunas personas no estarán de acuerdo con esta observación, ni con otras de sus opiniones. Pero una cosa sí está clara: Ray Suarez seguirá siendo muy visible, ayudando a su público a entender las personas y los eventos—extraordinarios y ordinarios—de su tiempo.

1 According to the article, how does Suarez stand out in his work in the broadcast news field?

   A. He can anticipate major political and social events.

   B. He can talk easily with both famous and ordinary people.

   C. He has an excellent memory and can make connections to other relevant topics.

   D. He doesn't get flustered in tense situations.

2 What did Suarez do during South Africa's first all-race elections that won him a major award?

   F. He eased tensions between the races.

   G. He interviewed people on the street.

   H. He made a documentary.

   I. He broadcast his show from South Africa for that special event.

3 According to the article, what honor did Suarez receive as a television news reporter at the end of the last century?

   A. A job as senior correspondent on *The NewsHour with Jim Lehrer*.

   B. The publication of his book, *The Old Neighborhood*.

   C. A prize for his help in establishing the Chicago Association of Hispanic Journalists.

   D. A second Alfred I. DuPont-Columbia University Silver Baton Award.

4 In *The Old Neighborhood*, what does Suarez say about Hispanic Americans?

   F. That they should be welcomed and supported as new immigrants.

   G. That they should learn English as soon as possible.

   H. That other Americans ignore their existence.

   I. That they should never forget their origins as they assimilate into the United States.

5   ¿Qué pregunta te gustaría hacerle a Ray Suarez?

6   ¿Qué es lo que más admiras de Ray Suarez? ¿Por qué? Usa información y detalles del artículo en tu respuesta.

Nombre: _____ Fecha: _____

1 Ⓐ Ⓑ Ⓒ Ⓓ   **2** Ⓕ Ⓖ Ⓗ Ⓘ   **3** Ⓐ Ⓑ Ⓒ Ⓓ

4 Ⓕ Ⓖ Ⓗ Ⓘ

5

| READ |
| THINK |
| EXPLAIN |

_____
_____
_____
_____
_____
_____

6

| READ |
| THINK |
| EXPLAIN |

_____
_____
_____
_____
_____
_____
_____
_____

STOP

Two Staples of Latin American Cuisine

Many basic foods popular today throughout the world were dietary staples of those who lived in the Americas long before the time of Columbus. Two such foods are beans and corn.

By far the most common main dish, or entrée, in Central America and parts of the Caribbean is black beans and rice. This combination is often served with a dry, white cheese on top and is accompanied by fried or boiled plantains (a less sweet variety of banana). This popular dish has acquired two very descriptive names. In Nicaragua it is known as *gallo pinto* (speckled rooster). In Costa Rica and Cuba it is called *moros y cristianos* (Moors and Christians), a reference to the period when Islamic Arabs ruled the European Christians of Spain.

Corn is key to a wide variety of Mexican and Central American dishes. It is the basis of the *tortilla de maíz,* which is used not only as a bread during meals, but is also a major ingredient in many of the region's best-known specialties: *tacos, enchiladas, tostadas, chilaquiles,* and even *sopa de tortilla.* Corn *tortillas* serve to thicken *moles* and stews and are used to scoop up beans, eggs, and salsas.

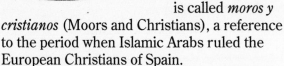

Tortillas are a staple throughout Mexico, and techniques of making them vary little from region to region. They can be made by hand at home or by a mechanical press in a *tortillería.* Essentially, however, *tortillas de maíz* are prepared in the same way as they were in the days of the Aztec empire. Flour *tortillas—tortillas de harina—*are an innovation developed after the Spaniards introduced wheat to the American continent.

Corn *tortillas* are made with white corn, slaked lime (a white powder obtained by exposing calcium hydroxide to moist air or water), and water. The washed corn is boiled in water with dissolved lime for about five minutes. After standing for several hours, it is rinsed, ground, and kneaded into dough *(masa).* Then the *tortillas* are shaped by hand. A small ball of *masa* is clapped back and forth from hand to hand to form a thin, flat circle. After this is done, the *tortilla* is baked on a griddle until it puffs in the center and turns a golden brown color. The *tortillas* of Central America, by the way, tend to be somewhat smaller and thicker than those popular in Mexico.

Another popular corn dish in Mexico and Central America is *tamales.* These can be sweet or spicy, wrapped in corn husks or banana leaves, and will vary in size and shape based on the region in which they are made.

But corn is not popular only as an ingredient of more complex dishes. In Ecuador, for example, *mote* is a typical part of family meals. *Mote* is nothing more than a platter of cooked large white corn kernels that is placed in the center of the table. Family members eat directly from the platter rather than using individual plates.

Test 34

1 Complete the following sentence: Beans and corn . . .

    A. were brought to the Americas by Columbus.

    B. are a common entrée in Central America and the Caribbean.

    C. were important foods in the Americas in pre-Columbian times.

    D. refer to the period of Moorish rule in Spain.

2 Based on the reading, which of the following best describes the use of *tortillas* in Mexican cooking?

    F. A thickening agent.

    G. A multi-purpose staple.

    H. The primary ingredient of *masa*.

    I. An edible scoop for salsa, etc.

3 Which one of the following statements is <u>not</u> true?

    A. *Tortillas* are made today following traditional methods.

    B. Flour and corn *tortillas* date to the time of the Aztecs.

    C. The size and shape of *tortillas* differ somewhat from region to region.

    D. *Tamales* are not made with *tortillas*.

4 Corn is the most widely used ingredient in Mexican cuisine. What would you say is the most widely used ingredient in the cuisine of the United States? List some of the foods of which the ingredient you chose is an important part.

5 **READ THINK EXPLAIN** Compare and contrast the uses of *tortillas* in Mexican cuisine and the uses of bread in the cuisine of the United States.

Nombre: _____ Fecha: _____

1 Ⓐ Ⓑ Ⓒ Ⓓ **2** Ⓕ Ⓖ Ⓗ Ⓘ **3** Ⓐ Ⓑ Ⓒ Ⓓ

4

READ
THINK
EXPLAIN

_____

_____

_____

_____

_____

_____

5

READ
THINK
EXPLAIN

_____

_____

_____

_____

_____

_____

_____

_____

STOP

Chilemanía

La palabra "chile" es del náhuatl *chilli*, y se usa para describir una planta de muchas variedades que originó en México. El chile fue una parte importante de la dieta de los antiguos mexicanos y lo prepararon en formas muy diferentes. Los españoles descubrieron esta planta cuando llegaron a las Américas. Cuando lo introdujeron a Europa después del primer viaje de Colón, en 1493, fue aceptado inmediatamente. Se considera una de las contribuciones más importantes del México prehispánico al mundo de la comida.

Pero ¿cómo son los chiles de hoy? ¿Son todos los chiles rojos y picantes? No. Hay chiles amarillos, verdes y de otros colores. También hay chiles menos picantes. Los chiles son muy populares en México, donde se cultivan más de cien variedades diferentes. Se cultivan todo el año y siempre es posible comprarlos en los mercados del país.

El chile es uno de los condimentos más usados en la preparación de la comida mexicana. Algunos de los platos que se asocian con las diferentes regiones de México usan chile como un ingrediente importante.

Por ejemplo, el estado de Puebla es famoso por *el mole poblano de guajolote,* un plato preparado con mole, una salsa hecha de chocolate y tres tipos de chiles: anchos, mulatos y pasillas. En el estado de Oaxaca, se come *pollo en pipián verde* preparado con una salsa hecha de dos tipos de chiles: poblanos y serranos. Usan chile ancho para dar el color rojo al *pozole rojo* que se prepara en el estado de Jalisco. Y en el estado de Veracruz, se prepara *huachinango a la veracruzana* con los chiles güeros.

Pero el chile no es sólo un condimento especial. Es el ingrediente principal en algunos platos típicamente mexicanos como *los chiles rellenos* y *los chiles en nogada.* Es verdad que el chile es sabroso, pero también es rico en las vitaminas C y A y tiene una cantidad bastante grande de algunos minerales. Y el chile es el complemento perfecto para una dieta alta en proteínas porque ayuda en la digestión de esta clase de comida. Es uno de los ingredientes que hace distintiva la comida mexicana.

1 Three of the following statements are false. Which one is true?

    A. The word *chile* comes from the name of the country.

    B. *Chiles* originated in Mexico and were an essential ingredient in the diet of pre-Columbian Mexicans.

    C. In pre-Columbian Mexico, people were limited in their methods of preparation of *chiles*.

    D. *Chiles* were not readily accepted when introduced into the European diet.

2 Which one of the following statements is <u>not</u> true?

    F. *Chiles* come in a variety of colors and some are less spicy than others.

    G. More than 100 types of *chile*s are available in Mexico.

    H. *Chiles* are found in many typical Mexican dishes.

    I. *Chiles* are seasonal and available only during certain times of the year.

3 Complete the following sentence. *El mole poblano de guajolote* is . . .

    A. turkey prepared with a sauce that contains two types of *chiles.*

    B. turkey prepared with a sauce that contains a red *chile* to give it its color.

    C. turkey prepared with a sauce that contains chocolate and three kinds of *chiles.*

    D. turkey prepared with a sauce for which the state of Jalisco is famous.

4 Based on the reading, which of the following best describes the use of *chiles* in Mexican cooking?

    F. They are used both as a condiment and as a main ingredient in some dishes.

    G. They are used primarily because of their nutritional value.

    H. They are used primarily because they complement other food groups such as proteins.

    I. They are used exclusively in regional dishes.

5 ¿Qué otras frutas o verduras tienen una variedad de formas y colores?

6   In large cities and in many regions of the United States, there are restaurants that serve ethnic food. Think about the restaurants in the city or region where you live. What kinds of ethnic food do they serve? If you have tasted food from one of these restaurants, how did you like it? If you haven't tasted any ethnic food, which would you like to taste? Explain your answer.

© Prentice-Hall, Inc.

Nombre: _____   Fecha: _____

1 Ⓐ Ⓑ Ⓒ Ⓓ   **2** Ⓕ Ⓖ Ⓗ Ⓘ   **3** Ⓐ Ⓑ Ⓒ Ⓓ

4 Ⓕ Ⓖ Ⓗ Ⓘ

5

READ
THINK
EXPLAIN

_____

_____

_____

_____

_____

_____

_____

6

READ
THINK
EXPLAIN

_____

_____

_____

_____

_____

_____

_____

_____

_____

_____

STOP

Restaurants

PASO A PASO 1	PASO A PASO 2	PASO A PASO 3
Chapter 12	Chapter 13	

Test **36**

Flan de piña

El flan es un postre de natillas (custard) cocidas en su propia salsa de caramelo. Es muy popular en España y en México, y también se encuentra en los restaurantes de cocina hispana en los Estados Unidos.

Los ingredientes típicos del flan son azúcar, leche y huevos. Pero hay muchas recetas para hacer el flan, con diferentes ingredientes, medidas, tiempos y temperaturas para cocinar, y recomendaciones sobre si es mejor prepararlo usando sólo el fuego de la estufa o el del horno también.

Esta receta contiene un ingrediente diferente muy sabroso y usa el fuego de la estufa y del horno. Como todo flan, éste se prepara en dos fases—primero el caramelo, y luego el flan.

Para hacer el caramelo

BATERÍA DE COCINA:

1 molde que se pueda calentar en la estufa

INGREDIENTES:

½ taza de azúcar
1 cucharada de agua

PREPARACIÓN:

1. Se mezcla el agua con el azúcar en el molde y se calienta a fuego lento en la estufa. Cuando la mezcla esté brillante, se sube el fuego y se hierve la mezcla por unos minutos.
2. Cuando la mezcla tenga el color café claro del caramelo, se quita del fuego. Se inclina el molde por todos lados para que el caramelo quede por todo el fondo y los lados del molde. Se cubre el molde.

¡Ojo! ¡El azúcar se pone muy caliente y puede quemarle!

Para hacer el flan

BATERÍA DE COCINA:

1 cacerola que resista el calor del horno
1 olla

INGREDIENTES:

1½ tazas de jugo de piña (en lata)
⅔ de taza de azúcar
6 huevos

PREPARACIÓN:

1. Se hierven el jugo de piña y el azúcar en una olla, de 5 a 10 minutos, y después se enfría la mezcla.
2. Se baten los huevos y poco a poco se agregan a la mezcla en la olla.
3. Se pone la mezcla en el molde, y luego se pone el molde entero en una cacerola resistente al calor del horno. Se le pone agua caliente a la cacerola (¡no al molde!) hasta que el molde esté rodeado de agua, pero no sumergido. Se pone la cacerola con el molde al horno a 325°F por 50 o 60 minutos.
4. Se saca la cacerola del horno. Se saca el molde del agua, se enfría un poco y se pone en el refrigerador.
5. Cuando sea conveniente, se saca el molde del refrigerador, y se saca el flan del molde.
6. Se sirve el flan en seguida, o se devuelve al refrigerador hasta la hora de servirlo.

¡Buen apetito!

© Prentice-Hall, Inc.

1 Which one of the following is <u>not</u> a typical ingredient of *flan*?

    A. Milk.

    B. Eggs.

    C. Sugar.

    D. Pineapple.

2 What do you think *"batería de cocina"* might mean?

    F. Pots and pans.

    G. Baking goods.

    H. Battery-operated small kitchen appliances.

    I. Basic cooking supplies.

3 According to the recipe, what do you have to watch out for as you are preparing the caramel?

    A. The caramel sauce might coat the bottom and sides of the mold.

    B. The sugar gets very hot and might burn you.

    C. The water might overflow from the pan holding the mold.

    D. The mix of sugar and water might get too bright and brittle.

4 Which kinds of heat are used for this recipe and when are they used?

    F. Stovetop only for the entire recipe.

    G. Oven only for the entire recipe.

    H. First oven, then stovetop.

    I. First stovetop, then oven.

5 READ THINK EXPLAIN

Nombra un ingrediente que te gustaría usar en una receta para flan. ¿En qué otros postres se usa ese ingrediente? ¿Es un ingrediente típico de postres americanos o de postres de otros países?

6 READ THINK EXPLAIN

What do you think is the most important advice to give someone writing a recipe? What is the most important advice to give someone following a recipe? Explain your answers.

© Prentice-Hall, Inc.

Nombre: _____   Fecha: _____

1 Ⓐ Ⓑ Ⓒ Ⓓ   **2** Ⓕ Ⓖ Ⓗ Ⓘ   **3** Ⓐ Ⓑ Ⓒ Ⓓ

4 Ⓕ Ⓖ Ⓗ Ⓘ

5

READ
THINK
EXPLAIN

_____
_____
_____
_____
_____
_____
_____

6

READ
THINK
EXPLAIN

_____
_____
_____
_____
_____
_____
_____
_____
_____
_____

STOP

El Niño and the Incan Legend of the Flood

What Is an El Niño?

An El Niño is a weather phenomenon that begins with a warming of the surface of the Pacific Ocean in the area around the equator. Its effects, which come much later, tend to be felt first in Ecuador and Peru, the two equatorial South American countries that jut furthest west into the ocean. It generally occurs in late December and thus bears the Spanish name for the Christ child—*El Niño*.

In the Pacific there is normally a strong east-to-west wind along the equator. This moves the water in a westerly direction. As that happens, in the East, colder water from below replaces the topmost water as it moves west. So you get water temperatures of about 30°C in the western Pacific and 20°C in the eastern Pacific near the coast of South America.

An El Niño brings weaker winds, so that colder water does not rise to the surface in the East. The warmer water that results makes the winds still weaker, which makes the ocean even warmer, which makes the winds even weaker, and so on.

Meanwhile, there are many different types of waves *beneath* the surface of the ocean, and they continue moving. Some are moving eastward toward Asia while others move westward toward the Americas. After a while they switch directions. All of this activity is constant and lasts many months. And, too, it goes pretty much unnoticed by all but meteorologists and oceanographers, who are getting better at predicting when an El Niño will develop.

The first results of an El Niño are unusually high rainfall and strong thunderstorms that move eastward through South America near the equator. It can be a blessing, causing more abundant crops for farmers, or it can be a nightmare, causing devastating floods. Gradually, El Niño's effects are felt elsewhere and may last for a year or more. In the United States, for example, they tend to cause wetter weather in the Southeast; in Australia they may cause drought.

El Niños occur irregularly, but on an average every three to seven years. The last five of the twentieth century were in 1972–73, 1977–78, 1982–83, 1991–92, and 1997–98.

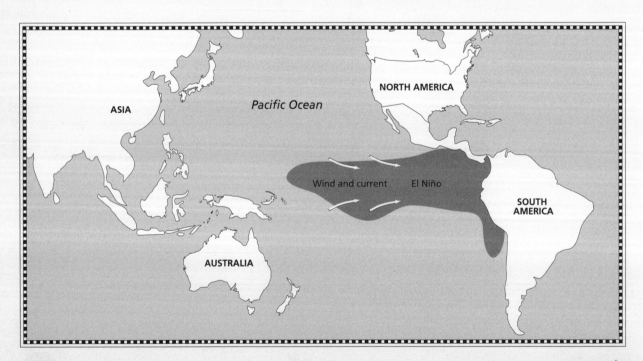

© Prentice-Hall, Inc.

The Incan Legend of the Flood

For obvious reasons, the Incas of Peru were strongly influenced by El Niño, and like many ancient peoples, they told a story about a catastrophic flood. Here is that Incan legend.

In ancient days, the elders would meet at the foot of the Andes mountains to discuss important matters. At that spot there grew a most remarkable tree—*el árbol de la vida*. It grew so high that its top reached far above the mountains and disappeared into the sky beyond. On the tree grew wonderful fruits of many different kinds, but they were too high for people to reach them. Those who tried to climb the Tree of Life invariably fell and died.

The animals, however, could climb the tree and enjoy the fruits. As they feasted, they taunted the humans below by throwing their garbage down on them. The people begged their chiefs to do something.

One night, one of the chiefs dreamed that he asked the Creator for an axe. The Creator agreed to give him one, but warned that using it on the Tree of Life would cause a catastrophe.

When he awoke, the chief was holding not an axe, but a parrot. Angrily he threw the parrot against the tree. The force of the blow caused a rain so strong that the ocean and rivers overflowed. Soon a flood covered the earth, destroying everything in sight.

Only one man survived the flood. As the waters rose higher and higher, he grasped the only thing that remained above water: the last remaining branch of the Tree of Life.

1 Why is this weather phenomenon called an El Niño?

    A. Because it usually begins around Christmas time in western South America.

    B. Because the Incas named it that.

    C. Because it reminded the people of the great flood.

    D. Because it occurs in Peru and Ecuador.

2 Three of the following statements are false. Which one is true?

    F. El Niños occur every year, but serious effects are only felt every three to seven years.

    G. El Niño's effects are felt only along the Pacific Coast of the Americas.

    H. El Niño's effects are felt first in Ecuador and Peru because they lie along the equator and are in the westernmost part of South America.

    I. There is no way of knowing in advance that an El Niño is developing because most of the wave activity is taking place below the surface of the ocean.

3 Which of the following is the first sign that an El Niño may eventually develop?

    A. A strong east-to-west wind that makes the water colder in the eastern Pacific.

    B. Unusually high rainfall and strong thunderstorms.

    C. At least three years have passed since the last El Niño.

    D. Continually weaker winds and warmer water in the eastern Pacific.

4 In the legend of the *árbol de la vida,* why did the people want to climb the tree?

    F. To kill the animals that were mocking them.

    G. To get at the fruits that were hanging from the tree.

    H. To save themselves from the flood.

    I. To have eternal life.

5 **READ THINK EXPLAIN** Many ancient cultures have legends concerning catastrophic floods. Do you think that the Incan story of the flood may have any basis in fact? Why or why not?

6 **READ THINK EXPLAIN** Compare and contrast the Incan legend of the flood with the story of Noah. In what ways are the stories similar? In what ways are they different?

Nombre: _____   Fecha: _____

1 Ⓐ Ⓑ Ⓒ Ⓓ   **2** Ⓕ Ⓖ Ⓗ Ⓘ   **3** Ⓐ Ⓑ Ⓒ Ⓓ

4 Ⓕ Ⓖ Ⓗ Ⓘ

5

READ
THINK
EXPLAIN

_____
_____
_____
_____
_____
_____

6

READ
THINK
EXPLAIN

_____
_____
_____
_____
_____
_____
_____
_____
_____

STOP

Dos maravillas ECOLÓGICAS *de* América Latina

El Parque Internacional La Amistad

Si visitas Costa Rica, puedes ver un sistema impresionante de parques nacionales, reservas indígenas y biológicas, y refugios para los animales salvajes. Gracias al Servicio de Parques Nacionales, que se estableció en 1970, más del 25 por ciento del país está reservado para conservación. Por eso muchas especies que están en peligro de extinción en los países cerca de Costa Rica pueden vivir aquí.

Uno de los parques nacionales más interesantes es El Parque Internacional La Amistad, la reserva natural más grande de Costa Rica. Se llama internacional porque una parte del parque está situada en el país de Panamá. Hay mucha diversidad de hábitats y especies en el parque porque existe una gran variedad de altitudes y climas en esta zona. En el parque viven cinco tipos de felinos: el jaguar, el puma, el margay, el ocelote y el jaguarundi. También hay más de 200 especies de reptiles y anfibios y más de 500 especies de pájaros.

Visitantes de todo el mundo van a Costa Rica todos los años para admirar esta maravilla tropical. Las visitas de estos turistas ayudan la economía del país y también contribuyen a la protección de sus recursos naturales.

Las Islas Galápagos

Ecuador, situado en la parte oeste de América del Sur, es el país más pequeño de la región de los Andes. Gracias a su clima agradable y sus diversos hábitats, tiene una de las colecciones más extraordinarias de plantas y animales exóticos de todo el mundo. Las Islas Galápagos, situadas en el océano Pacífico, a dos millas de la costa, forman parte de Ecuador.

Las Islas Galápagos son un parque nacional ecuatoriano y son famosas por habitantes como los pingüinos, iguanas y tortugas gigantes, muchos de los cuales están en peligro de extinción. Para conservar el ecosistema del parque, hoy día se limita el número de personas que pueden visitarlo cada año. También se usa el dinero del turismo para proteger las diferentes especies que viven allí.

A los científicos les interesa mucho la flora y fauna de las

Islas Galápagos. Charles Darwin, el primer visitante europeo a las Islas en 1835, descubrió que muchos de los animales y pájaros eran diferentes de las especies en otras partes del mundo. Sus observaciones de las especies en las islas lo ayudaron a formular su teoría para explicar la selección natural.

© Prentice-Hall, Inc.

1 According to the reading, why is it possible for such a wide variety of species to exist in El Parque Internacional La Amistad?

    A.   The National Park Service imports exotic species from other countries.

    B.   It includes areas that have significant differences in altitude and climate.

    C.   Part of the park is in Costa Rica and part is in Panama.

    D.   Five zones of life are found in the park.

2 According to the reading, why is it beneficial for the Galapagos Islands to be designated a national park?

    F.   It allows the park authorities to protect the ecosystem by limiting the number of visitors.

    G.   It allows the park authorities to charge more for admission.

    H.   It allows the park authorities to hire more park-certified guides.

    I.   It makes it more attractive as a tourist destination.

3 Which of the following is something that El Parque Internacional La Amistad and the Galapagos Islands do not have in common?

    A.   Both are national parks.

    B.   Both are among the most frequently visited sites in their respective countries.

    C.   Both are associated with studies conducted by well-known scientists.

    D.   Both are home to diverse habitats and species.

4 READ THINK EXPLAIN   ¿Por qué crees que algunos de los animales de las Islas Galápagos están en peligro de extinción?

5 READ THINK EXPLAIN   ¿Por qué es bueno y malo para estas dos atracciones turísticas ser tan populares?

Nombre: _____ Fecha: _____

1 (A) (B) (C) (D) **2** (F) (G) (H) (I) **3** (A) (B) (C) (D)

4

READ
THINK
EXPLAIN

_____
_____
_____
_____
_____
_____

5

READ
THINK
EXPLAIN

_____
_____
_____
_____
_____
_____
_____
_____
_____

STOP

Greenpeace
en el mundo hispano

Greenpeace es una organización internacional que trabaja para proteger el medio ambiente y para mantener el equilibrio ecológico del mundo. La organización se dedica a actividades como las siguientes: reducir el número de barcos de pesca para proteger la biodiversidad marina; eliminar contaminación del aire y del agua para proteger la salud de los seres humanos y de los animales; eliminar el uso de fuentes de energía tradicionales, como petróleo, carbón y gas natural, y usar fuentes renovables, como solar o del viento, para evitar peligrosos cambios en el clima.

A proteger el Mediterráneo

El mar Mediterráneo está en peligro. Los grupos ecologistas como Greenpeace-España están haciendo una campaña ecológica para proteger los peces y otros animales marinos y también a la gente que va a la playa. Treinta personas trabajan para la organización. También hay muchos jóvenes voluntarios que ayudan a Greenpeace.

Según Xavier Pastor, presidente de Greenpeace-España, se prohibe bañarse en algunas playas españolas porque hay bacterias en el agua que enferman a la gente. Para resolver este problema, el señor Pastor recomienda la eliminación de los ácidos que usa la industria del papel porque éstos contaminan el mar. Para proteger los peces y otros animales marinos, Greenpeace captura los barcos de pesca ilegales. La Unión Europea sólo permite a los pescadores capturar un número determinado de peces. Greenpeace usa un barco y un helicóptero para buscar a los pescadores que capturan demasiados peces.

A proteger las costas de México

Hay problemas ecológicos en México también. Los grupos ecologistas creen que la muerte de muchas ballenas cerca de las costas de México se debe a la contaminación del agua por pesticidas y basura. Y esta contaminación también puede hacer daño a los seres humanos si comen mariscos del área contaminada. Según Roberto López, representante de Greenpeace-México, el golfo de California en particular está muy contaminado. Su organización recomienda una investigación para determinar la causa de la contaminación. Greenpeace-México también protesta contra el echar de materiales tóxicos cerca de la costa del golfo de México. Se dice que Pemex, el mayor productor de petróleo en México, echa estos materiales en los ríos y por eso el agua está contaminada.

1 According to the article, which of the following is <u>not</u> one of Greenpeace's environmental objectives?

    A. To protect the health of humans and animals by eliminating pollutants.

    B. To prevent dangerous climactic changes by phasing out fossil fuels and replacing them with renewable energy sources.

    C. To safeguard marine biodiversity by reducing the number of fishing boats.

    D. To change the world's ecological balance.

2 What solutions has Greenpeace-España proposed for Spain's environmental problems?

    F. Eliminating the use of acids by the paper industry to avoid contamination of the water.

    G. Hiring more volunteers to work with their organization.

    H. Capturing fishing boats that catch less than the allowable number of fish.

    I. Not allowing people to swim at beaches with contaminated water.

3 Which of the following pollutants was <u>not</u> mentioned as a possible cause for the environmental problems along Mexico's coasts?

    A. Pesticides and garbage.

    B. Toxic waste.

    C. Coal.

    D. Petroleum.

4 Imagina que un(a) ecólogo(a) famoso(a) va a visitar tu escuela. Escribe tres preguntas que te gustaría hacerle sobre su profesión. Piensa en algunos de los problemas ecológicos mencionados en la lectura para ayudarte a escribir tus preguntas.

5 Para celebrar el Día de la Tierra, cada estudiante va a escribir un párrafo para la revista literaria escolar sobre lo que hace su comunidad para proteger el medio ambiente. Antes de escribir tu párrafo, haz una lista de lo que hace tu comunidad. Después, escribe un párrafo de por lo menos cinco o seis frases. No olvides de mencionar lo que tu familia y tu escuela hacen para proteger el medio ambiente.

Nombre: _____ Fecha: _____

1 Ⓐ Ⓑ Ⓒ Ⓓ   **2** Ⓕ Ⓖ Ⓗ Ⓘ   **3** Ⓐ Ⓑ Ⓒ Ⓓ

4

READ
THINK
EXPLAIN

_____
_____
_____
_____
_____
_____

5

READ
THINK
EXPLAIN

_____
_____
_____
_____
_____
_____
_____
_____
_____
_____

STOP

Los hispanohablantes y la Internet

En 1969, cuando se creó la Internet en California, pocos se imaginaban que dentro de unos treinta años transformaría totalmente el estilo de vida de personas en todo el mundo. En esa época, la Internet era exclusivamente un medio de comunicación para universidades, gobiernos y agencias internacionales, principalmente en los Estados Unidos. Pero hoy día, la Internet no es nada exclusiva. Con la tecnología necesaria, todo el mundo puede usarla. Y la Internet sirve para una infinidad de cosas—para hacer compras, divertirse, educarse, trabajar desde casa y mucho más. En más y más países del mundo, sobre todo los países en que se habla español (y entre éstos se incluye los Estados Unidos), esto es precisamente lo que está pasando.

Según un estudio de International Data Corporation, al final del año 1999 había más de 8.5 millones de usuarios de Internet en Latinoamérica. Éste es un aumento de 49 por ciento sobre los 5.7 millones de usuarios en 1998. Otro estudio indica que la cantidad combinada de usuarios hispanohablantes en los Estados Unidos y Latinoamérica pronto llegará a más de 38 millones. Al sumarse este número con los dos millones de usuarios en España, la cantidad total de hispanohablantes usando la Internet en el año 2000 ya está a (o pronto será) más de 40 millones, o aproximadamente un cuarto de la cantidad de usuarios en todo el mundo.

Es difícil calcular y predecir la cantidad de usuarios de la Internet porque a veces crece de una manera tan fantástica que parece una mentira. En sólo nueve meses de 1995, por ejemplo, la cantidad de sitios comerciales en la Internet en México creció mil por ciento. Pero una predicción que sí es constante y segura es que para el año 2002, el inglés ya no será el idioma dominante de la Internet. Se anticipa que va a haber más usuarios de la Internet que hablan otros idiomas que el inglés—el español sí, pero también otros idiomas de todos los países del mundo.

Para los usuarios hispanohablantes de la Internet, hay una explosión de portales (sitios que sirven como puerta a la Internet). En los Estados Unidos, dos de los portales en español más conocidos son StarMedia.com de Nueva York y Yupi.com de la Florida (su nombre es la traducción al español de *"yippee"*). Dos portales en inglés, Yahoo y Prodigy, también tienen versiones en español: espanol.yahoo.com y espanol.prodigy.com. También hay portales en español en España y Latinoamérica, por supuesto; por ejemplo, elsitio.com de Argentina y to2.com de México.

La rivalidad entre estos portales para atraer usuarios hispanohablantes es bastante fuerte. Algunos portales también ofrecen información en inglés para los hispanohablantes que prefieren comunicarse en los dos idiomas. Tres portales bilingües son QuePasa.com de Arizona, oyeme.com de New Jersey y latinolink.com de California. También hay portales sólo en inglés con temas de interés para los hispanos, como latinobeat.net de California y hisp.com de la Florida.

El encuentro del inglés y el español con la Internet resultó en la creación de otro idioma, el "ciberspanglish." A algunas personas no les gusta nada este nuevo idioma, pero otras no ven ningún problema con mezclar los idiomas para comunicarse mejor. Algunos términos comunes del ciberspanglish son "jom peich," "emailear," "forwardear," "spamear" y "downloadear." Para los que quieren mantener el español puro, hay traducciones muy precisas y útiles de términos comunes, como "globos de ayuda" *(balloon help)*, "flujo de datos" *(data flow)*, "motor de búsqueda" *(search engine)* y "estación de trabajo" *(work station)*.

1 Which one of the following did <u>not</u> use the Internet in the early years after its creation?

    A. Universities.

    B. Businesses.

    C. Government agencies.

    D. International agencies.

2 According to the article, why is it so difficult to calculate and predict the number of users of the Internet?

    F. Because information on this is false or not reliable.

    G. Because the Internet is used worldwide and it's hard to keep track of its users.

    H. Because the number of users is constantly increasing so dramatically.

    I. Because not all of the users speak English.

3 What change in Internet use is expected to take place by 2002?

    A. Most of the users will not be English speakers.

    B. All countries in the world will have Internet access.

    C. The Internet will be available to speakers of all known languages.

    D. Most of the users will be Spanish speakers.

4 Which one of the following portals is <u>not</u> in Spanish?

    F. Latinolink.com of California.

    G. QuePasa.com of Arizona.

    H. StarMedia.com of New York.

    I. Hisp.com of Florida.

5 **READ THINK EXPLAIN** ¿Por qué crees que la gente usa el ciberspanglish?

6 **READ THINK EXPLAIN** The name of the Mexican portal mentioned in the reading—to2.com—might be called a "visual pun." Write down the name the way it would be said in Spanish. Why is this a good name for an Internet portal?

The following imaginary Web sites are also visual puns. Match each site with the description of what it might contain. Next to each answer, write the name of the site without using the visual pun.

    1 100cias.com   **a)** a site that offers information on the care of pet fish

    2 co1/2s.com   **b)** a site where you can find humorous videos

    3 p6.com   **c)** a site where you can buy T-shirts

    4 camiZ.com   **d)** a site containing information about the sciences

Nombre: _____   Fecha: _____

1 Ⓐ Ⓑ Ⓒ Ⓓ   **2** Ⓕ Ⓖ Ⓗ Ⓘ   **3** Ⓐ Ⓑ Ⓒ Ⓓ

4 Ⓕ Ⓖ Ⓗ Ⓘ

5

READ
THINK
EXPLAIN

_____
_____
_____
_____

6

READ
THINK
EXPLAIN

_____
_____
_____
_____

Write the letter of the description that matches the site, then write the name of the site without using the visual pun.

1 100cias.com   _____   _____

2 co1/2s.com   _____   _____

3 p6.com   _____   _____

4 camiZ.com   _____   _____

STOP

Guernica:
La pintura como protesta

En julio de 1936, unos oficiales del ejército español se rebelaron contra el gobierno. Los habitantes del país se dividieron, y hubo una guerra civil terrible que duró hasta 1939. Murieron más de un millón de personas.

El 26 de abril de 1937, un pequeño pueblo en el norte de España fue bombardeado. Aunque el lugar no tenía ningún valor militar, el ataque duró tres horas y murieron 1.645 personas.

En todas partes del mundo la gente reaccionó contra ese ataque. Protestaron, escribieron artículos, y algunos fueron a España a luchar, incluso un grupo de norteamericanos que se llamaba The Abraham Lincoln Brigade. Una de las muchas obras literarias escritas sobre esa guerra fue la novela famosa de Ernest Hemingway, *Por quién doblan las campanas.*

Una persona que respondió a ese evento de una manera personal fue el pintor español Pablo Picasso, que en aquel tiempo vivía en París. En esa época era probablemente el artista más conocido del mundo. Fue el creador del cubismo y gran explorador de nuevos estilos y técnicas. Su reacción fue, ese mismo verano, la creación de una pintura para la sección del gobierno español en la Feria Mundial de París. Esa obra representaba la masacre de Guernica, ese pueblito al norte de España.

El *Guernica* de Picasso no es una pintura realista, pero tampoco es difícil de comprender. Una bombilla eléctrica ilumina la escena como una explosión. Figuras de personas y animales se mezclan en el horror. Una mujer llora por su bebé muerto. Otras dos corren por la calle, y otra, con una lámpara en la mano, mira la masacre desde una ventana. Hay un hombre muerto, caído en el suelo. Un caballo relincha con terror. A un lado hay un toro, quizás el símbolo de España misma.

La composición del *Guernica* contiene mucha fuerza expresiva. Parece una explosión que empieza en el centro del cuadro. El efecto de destrucción es aumentado por las formas afiladas, que nos recuerdan los dientes de una sierra—o de un animal feroz. Picasso no necesitó usar colores para hacernos sentir el terror y el dolor. No vemos ni el amarillo de las explosiones ni el rojo de la sangre o del fuego. Todo está representado en blanco, negro y gris.

El *Guernica,* más que una ilustración de un evento particular, es un símbolo universal de los horrores de la guerra, de todo lo que sufre la gente cuando se encuentra entre ejércitos que luchan por el poder.

Durante la Segunda Guerra Mundial, se llevó la pintura al museo de Arte Moderno de Nueva York. Permaneció allí hasta 1981, cuando la llevaron a España, donde el museo del Prado creó un edificio especial para exponerla.

1 Against whom did the army rebel?

    A. The Spanish government.

    B. A small town in the north of Spain.

    C. The population that was fighting the civil war.

    D. The foreigners who came to Spain to fight.

2 Which one of the following is <u>not</u> mentioned as being depicted in Picasso's *Guernica?*

    F. A terrified horse whinnying.

    G. Serrated shapes that remind the viewer of the teeth of a saw.

    H. A soldier with a sword.

    I. A woman crying for her dead baby.

3 According to the reading, why is the painting such a universally known landmark in the history of art?

    A. It is realistic and easy to understand.

    B. It symbolizes for everyone the horrors of war.

    C. It is a symbol of Spain itself.

    D. It illustrates a particular event in history.

4 What is one of the most remarkable facts about the painting?

    F. It inspired the novel *For Whom the Bell Tolls.*

    G. It is entirely in shades of black, gray, and white.

    H. It has been shown in Paris, New York, and Madrid.

    I. The painter was a Spaniard living in France.

5 READ THINK EXPLAIN

Usa información y detalles del artículo para hacer una lista de algunas de las cosas que la gente de todas partes del mundo hizo en reacción contra la guerra civil española.

6 READ THINK EXPLAIN

Describe un evento especialmente emocionante o importante que conoces. Imagina que vas a representarlo en una obra de arte. ¿Qué símbolos usarás? ¿Usarás colores o materiales especiales o una técnica especial? Si es posible, dibuja la obra que te gustaría crear.

Nombre: _____ Fecha: _____

1 Ⓐ Ⓑ Ⓒ Ⓓ   **2** Ⓕ Ⓖ Ⓗ Ⓘ   **3** Ⓐ Ⓑ Ⓒ Ⓓ

4 Ⓕ Ⓖ Ⓗ Ⓘ

5

READ
THINK
EXPLAIN

_____
_____
_____
_____
_____
_____
_____

6

READ
THINK
EXPLAIN

_____
_____
_____
_____
_____
_____
_____
_____
_____
_____

STOP

Una leyenda afrocubana

Los esclavos africanos que fueron llevados a Cuba en el siglo XVI contaron historias fantásticas llamadas *patakines* para conservar sus tradiciones y creencias. Éstas sirvieron para enseñar lecciones sobre la vida. La siguiente historia nos relata cómo el dios Obatalá escogió a la mejor persona para ser líder de todo el mundo.

Hace mucho tiempo, Obatalá observó que Orula era muy imaginativo. En más de una ocasión pensó que podía ser líder de todo el mundo, pero al pensarlo con cuidado decidió que Orula era demasiado joven para una misión de tanta importancia. Un día, Obatalá quiso saber si Orula era tan capaz como parecía, y le dijo:

—Prepárame la mejor comida posible.

Orula escuchó lo que le pidió Obatalá y, sin responder, fue directamente al mercado para comprar una lengua de toro. La preparó usando condimentos y la cocinó de una manera tan singular que Obatalá se la comió. Cuando terminó la comida, Obatalá le preguntó por qué la lengua era la mejor comida que se podía preparar. Orula respondió a Obatalá:

—Con la lengua se considera todos los aspectos de una discusión, se proclama la virtud, se exaltan las obras y maneras, y también se dicen cosas muy buenas sobre las personas . . .

Cuando pasó algún tiempo, Obatalá le dijo a Orula:

—Prepárame otra comida, pero esta vez debe ser la peor comida posible.

Orula regresó al mercado, compró otra lengua de toro, la cocinó y se la presentó a Obatalá.

Cuando Obatalá vio la misma comida, le dijo:

—¡Orula!, ¿cómo es posible? Cuando me serviste esta comida antes me dijiste que era la mejor, y ahora me la presentas como la peor.

Orula respondió a Obatalá:

—Es verdad que antes te dije que era la mejor. Pero ahora te digo que es la peor, porque con ella se vende y se pierde a todos los habitantes de una comunidad, se dicen malas cosas contra las personas, se destruye su buena reputación y se hacen las acciones más crueles que sean posibles.

Obatalá, maravillado de la inteligencia y precocidad de Orula, lo proclamó líder de todo el mundo.

© Prentice-Hall, Inc.

1 Why did Obatalá order Orula to cook the best meal possible?

    A. To prove that he was the best chef around.

    B. To prove that he was capable of finding a market that sold the best ingredients.

    C. To prove that he was capable of ruling the entire world.

    D. To prove that he was too young to cook such a meal.

2 According to Orula, what was one reason why the bull's tongue was the best meal?

    F. It was prepared with the right condiments.

    G. It was prepared in a special way.

    H. It allowed someone to say nice things about himself or herself.

    I. It allowed someone to weigh all sides of an issue.

3 According to Orula, what was one reason why the bull's tongue was also the worst meal?

    A. It was purchased from a different market.

    B. It was served without cooking it.

    C. It allowed someone to do the cruelest things possible.

    D. It prevented someone from saying uncomplimentary things about others.

4 READ THINK EXPLAIN ¿Qué crees que simboliza la lengua en esta leyenda? ¿Qué moraleja crees que enseña esta leyenda?

5 READ THINK EXPLAIN ¿En qué se parecen esta leyenda y otras que conoces?

Nombre: _____   Fecha: _____

1 Ⓐ Ⓑ Ⓒ Ⓓ   **2** Ⓕ Ⓖ Ⓗ Ⓘ   **3** Ⓐ Ⓑ Ⓒ Ⓓ

4

READ
THINK
EXPLAIN

_____
_____
_____
_____
_____
_____

5

READ
THINK
EXPLAIN

_____
_____
_____
_____
_____
_____
_____
_____
_____

STOP

Organizaciones
de voluntarios

Hay muchas organizaciones en las que puedes trabajar como voluntario(a) para ayudar
a los demás, en tu comunidad o en otros países del mundo. Cuando ayudas a las
personas, también te ayudas a ti mismo(a) porque conoces nuevos países, situaciones y personas.
Aquí tienes dos ejemplos de organizaciones de voluntarios.

Peace Corps

Esta es una organización de voluntarios que estableció el Congreso de los Estados Unidos hace 40 años. Su misión es trabajar por la paz y el entendimiento en todo el mundo. Esta organización envía a personas entrenadas como voluntarios a los países necesitados e interesados en el programa. Las áreas en las que la organización puede ayudar son educación, medio ambiente, salud, agricultura y economía.

Muchos jóvenes norteamericanos sirven como voluntarios para el Peace Corps; entre 1961 y 1999, 140.000 voluntarios sirvieron en más de 100 países de África, América Central, América del Sur, Asia y Europa. Estos jóvenes ayudan a la gente y también aprenden mucho sobre la cultura y la lengua del país en el que están situados. Los voluntarios reciben tres meses de entrenamiento y después viven por dos años en el país asignado. Muchos voluntarios repiten la experiencia varias veces.

Una joven que sirvió como voluntaria en Paraguay describe su experiencia en este pequeño país sudamericano:

—Cuando llegué a Paraguay, trabajé como consultora para un nuevo programa para enseñar a los niños preescolares. En el pasado, no hubo programas como éste y los niños entraron en el primer grado sin ninguna preparación. Muchos de éstos sólo hablaban guaraní y como resultado tuvieron que quedarse en este grado por más de un año porque les faltaba preparación adecuada. Después de trabajar en ese programa por dos años, decidí quedarme en Paraguay por un año más. Trabajé como coordinadora de un programa de la salud para la oficina del Peace Corps en Asunción. En este trabajo, viajé a diferentes lugares para ayudar a los nuevos

voluntarios. Y durante los últimos tres meses, trabajé para establecer un nuevo proyecto para los jóvenes. Para mí, la experiencia de ser voluntaria para el Peace Corps fue una de las más difíciles de toda mi vida pero también una de las más importantes.

AmeriCorps

AmeriCorps es una organización de voluntarios que trabajan en las comunidades urbanas y rurales de los Estados Unidos. En 1993, el Presidente Clinton firmó el *National and Community Service Trust Act* que estableció la *Corporation for National Service,* una corporación encargada de servir a las comunidades de los Estados Unidos.

En 1994, los primeros voluntarios empezaron a servir en más de 1.000 comunidades. En los primeros cinco años, más de 100.000 voluntarios enseñaron a los niños a leer, hicieron más seguras las comunidades, ayudaron a las víctimas de desastres naturales y participaron en otras actividades que beneficiaron a personas y comunidades necesitadas. Después de terminar su servicio, casi el 99 por ciento de los voluntarios para AmeriCorps dicen que piensan seguir sirviendo a la comunidad.

Una voluntaria describe sus sentimientos sobre servir a la comunidad: "Antes de trabajar como voluntaria para AmeriCorps, nunca hice servicio comunitario. Ahora pienso dedicarme a hacerlo cuando tenga tiempo libre."

Otro voluntario dice: "No sabía nada sobre organizaciones como AmeriCorps. Creo que AmeriCorps me enseñó cómo funciona esta clase de organizaciones."

Pues, otra ventaja de servir como voluntario para AmeriCorps es obtener habilidades que se pueden usar en el mundo del trabajo.

1 Which one of the following is <u>not</u> an area in which the Peace Corps offers assistance?

    A. Education.   **C.** Environment.

    B. Health.   **D.** Athletic training.

2 Three of the following statements are false. Which one is true?

    F. Peace Corps volunteers don't learn about other cultures and languages.

    G. Peace Corps volunteers receive no special training.

    H. Peace Corps volunteers serve throughout the world.

    I. Peace Corps volunteers usually serve for a period of three years.

3 Why was AmeriCorps created?

    A. To compete with the Peace Corps.

    B. To provide community-service opportunities in the U.S.

    C. To provide community-service opportunities throughout the world.

    D. To provide job-training opportunities for interested citizens.

4 According to the article, which of the following is <u>not</u> one of the advantages of joining AmeriCorps?

    F. Learning to speak another language.

    G. Getting involved in community-service programs.

    H. Learning skills that may be valuable to employers.

    I. Motivating others to participate in community-service activities.

5 Three of the following statements are true. Which one is false?

    A. Peace Corps and AmeriCorps volunteers often choose to extend their service.

    B. Peace Corps and AmeriCorps volunteers participate in community-service activities that improve the quality of life for others.

    C. Peace Corps and AmeriCorps have been in existence for more than 40 years.

    D. Peace Corps and AmeriCorps were created by Acts of Congress.

6 READ THINK EXPLAIN ¿Por qué crees que la experiencia de la voluntaria en Paraguay fue tan difícil para ella?

7 READ THINK EXPLAIN Imagina que quieres trabajar como voluntario(a) para una de estas dos organizaciones. ¿Para cuál te gustaría trabajar? ¿Por qué?

Nombre: _____   Fecha: _____

1 Ⓐ Ⓑ Ⓒ Ⓓ   **2** Ⓕ Ⓖ Ⓗ Ⓘ   **3** Ⓐ Ⓑ Ⓒ Ⓓ

4 Ⓕ Ⓖ Ⓗ Ⓘ   **5** Ⓐ Ⓑ Ⓒ Ⓓ

6

READ
THINK
EXPLAIN

_____
_____
_____
_____
_____
_____

7

READ
THINK
EXPLAIN

_____
_____
_____
_____
_____
_____
_____
_____
_____
_____

STOP

La herencia hispana
en los Estados Unidos

**En los Estados Unidos hay muchos pueblos y ciudades
que tienen una importante herencia hispana y que hoy día tienen una población hispana
bastante grande. Aquí tienes cuatro ejemplos.**

San Diego

San Diego es la segunda ciudad más grande del estado de California y la sexta más grande de los Estados Unidos. Tiene más de un millón de habitantes. Muchas veces se dice que San Diego es el lugar donde empezó el estado de California. En 1542 Juan Rodríguez Cabrillo llegó a este lugar, que no se llamó San Diego hasta sesenta años más tarde. En 1769 Fray Junípero Serra fundó allí la primera de sus nueve misiones en California. Hoy día es una ciudad importante por el turismo y la industria de las computadoras.

St. Augustine (*San Agustín*)

Esta ciudad está en el noreste de la Florida, en la costa del océano Atlántico. San Agustín fue el primer sitio permanente fundado por los españoles en el territorio que hoy es los Estados Unidos.

Empezó como una misión religiosa fundada en 1565 por el español Pedro Menéndez de Avilés. Hoy día es una ciudad de 12.000 habitantes, más o menos, que vive del turismo. San Agustín todavía conserva un centro antiguo donde se pueden ver arquitectura colonial muy bonita y la iglesia de la antigua misión.

Santa Fe

Santa Fe fue fundada en 1609 como la capital de la colonia española de Nuevo México. En aquel tiempo, Santa Fe era una ciudad muy importante para el comercio entre todas las colonias españolas del continente americano, porque aquí terminaba el Camino Real, una "carretera" que empezaba en Perú y pasaba por todo el continente. Hoy es una ciudad que está de moda porque su vida cultural es muy interesante. Muchos artistas y artesanos viven allí. A los turistas les encanta Santa Fe por sus museos, galerías de arte y exposiciones de arte

indígena. Todavía conserva su identidad colonial española en su arquitectura y en su modo de vida.

Laredo

Esta ciudad está al sur del estado de Texas, al lado del Río Grande. El 90 por ciento de sus habitantes son hispanos. Laredo fue el primer sitio fundado por los españoles en los Estados Unidos, en 1755, que no era ni religioso ni militar. Después de la guerra de 1848 entre México y los Estados Unidos, cuando se estableció la frontera entre los dos países, los habitantes de Laredo que querían ser mexicanos fundaron la ciudad de Nuevo Laredo, al otro lado del Río Grande, en México. Hoy día, Laredo está creciendo más rápidamente que ninguna otra ciudad en Texas. Todavía conserva su centro histórico y antiguo de tradición española, que incluye el mercado y la iglesia de San Agustín.

1 What types of buildings typically remain as remnants of this country's Spanish heritage?

    A. Business establishments.

    B. Educational institutions.

    C. Municipal buildings.

    D. Churches.

2 Based on the reading, which one of the following statements is <u>not</u> true?

    F. All four cities are important to the economy of their states.

    G. All four cities were initially religious centers or missions.

    H. All four cities have preserved their Spanish heritage through architecture.

    I. All four cities are located in states with large Spanish-speaking populations.

3 Which of the cities mentioned in the reading received its present name sixty years after it was founded?

    A. San Diego.

    B. Laredo.

    C. St. Augustine.

    D. Santa Fe.

4 Imagina que es 1848 y que vives en la región de la nueva frontera entre los Estados Unidos y México. ¿Dónde prefieres vivir, en Nuevo Laredo o en Laredo? Explica tu respuesta.

5 ¿Hay ejemplos de la herencia hispana en tu comunidad? ¿Cuáles son? Si no hay ejemplos, ¿por qué no existen?

Nombre: _____ Fecha: _____

1 Ⓐ Ⓑ Ⓒ Ⓓ   **2** Ⓕ Ⓖ Ⓗ Ⓘ   **3** Ⓐ Ⓑ Ⓒ Ⓓ

4

READ
THINK
EXPLAIN

_____

_____

_____

_____

_____

_____

5

READ
THINK
EXPLAIN

_____

_____

_____

_____

_____

_____

_____

_____

STOP